INSTRUCTOR'S MANUAL

KENNETH G. PINZKE

APPLICATIONS AND INVESTIGATIONS IN

EARTH SCIENCE

Fourth Edition

TARBUCK

LUTGENS

PINZKE

Upper Saddle River, NJ 07458

Editor in Chief: Sheri Snavely
Senior Acquisitions Editor: Patrick Lynch
Supplement Editor: Melanie Van Benthuysen
Executive Managing Editor: Kathleen Schiaparelli
Assistant Managing Editor: Dinah Thong
Production Editor: Megan L. Williams
Supplement Cover Management/Design: Paul Gourhan
Manufacturing Buyer: Ilene Kahn

© 2003 by Pearson Education, Inc.
Pearson Education, Inc.
Upper Saddle River, NJ 07458

The author and publisher of this book have used their best efforts in preparing this book. These efforts include the development, research, and testing of the theories and programs to determine their effectiveness. The author and publisher make no warranty of any kind, expressed or implied, with regard to these programs or the documentation contained in this book. The author and publisher shall not be liable in any event for incidental or consequential damages in connection with, or arising out of, the furnishing, performance, or use of these programs.

Printed in the United States of America

10 9 8 7 6 5 4 3 2
ISBN 0-13-046096-6

Pearson Education Ltd., *London*
Pearson Education Australia Pty. Ltd., *Sydney*
Pearson Education Singapore, Pte. Ltd.
Pearson Education North Asia Ltd., *Hong Kong*
Pearson Education Canada, Inc., *Toronto*
Pearson Educacíon de Mexico, S.A. de C.V.
Pearson Education—Japan, *Tokyo*
Pearson Education Malaysia, Pte. Ltd.
Pearson Education, *Upper Saddle River, New Jersey*

CONTENTS

PREFACE

Applications and Investigations in Earth Science, Fourth Edition, is designed to supplement an introductory general education Earth science course. The manual includes exercises that survey most of the major topics in Earth science, building upon questions that require various levels of understanding to answer. Recognizing that different aspects of Earth science are emphasized by each of us, twenty-two exercises that cover a wide variety of subjects are included in the manual. Since each is basically self-contained and covers a specific topic, individual topics or whole sections can be omitted or introduced in a different sequence without difficulty. Furthermore, with only minor modification, several exercises, or portions of exercises, may be assigned for completion outside the regularly scheduled laboratory sessions.

Many of the exercises require that equipment and materials be supplied and present in the laboratory. When needed, a general list has been included at the beginning of each exercise. Also, to assist you in preparing to use the manual, a comprehensive list of the materials, supplies, and equipment (including vendors and addresses) necessary to complete all the exercises is included with this instructor's manual.

To assist you in preparing for and using *Applications and Investigations in Earth Science*, Fourth Edition, the following general suggestions, recommendations, and guidelines may be helpful.

- A list of recommended student-furnished materials is included with the materials list provided in this instructor's manual. In addition to their textbook and class notes, students should purchase and bring these materials to laboratory sessions. We recommend that a list of all student-furnished materials be given to each student at the beginning of the course.

- Students should be encouraged to read the required text assignment, examine the exercise, and gather their materials prior to beginning each exercise.

- We recommend that the Summary/Report page included with each exercise be completed and submitted by each student at a designated time following the assignment of the exercise.

- Exercises Twenty-one, "Location and Distance on Earth," and Twenty-two, "The Metric System, Measurements, and Scientific Inquiry" involve basic Earth science skills used throughout the manual. Should you decide to do either, or both, we recommend that they be done early in the term.

- Exercise Seventeen, "Astronomical Observations," will require several weeks for a student to complete. The information gathered in the exercise is applicable to, although not necessary for completion of, several other exercises.

- Realizing that some laboratory settings have limited materials such as minerals, rocks, and fossils, we have left the specific choices of these specimens to the instructor.

- In recognition of the fact that there is a vast amount of material to be presented in an introductory Earth science course and the time constraints that this can impose, instructors should examine each exercise closely and if necessary modify it to meet their specific needs.

- The answers to the questions for each exercise that are provided in this instructor's manual are presented in a manner that allows the pages to be removed, duplicated, and posted for student review.

In summary, we feel that through the active student participation offered by each of the exercises in *Applications and Investigations in Earth Science* the learning process is carried one step closer to complete understanding.

MATERIALS, SUPPLIES, AND EQUIPMENT

Following is a complete list of the materials, supplies, and equipment necessary to furnish an introductory Earth science laboratory for use with the laboratory manual *Applications and Investigations in Earth Science*. The list has been divided into three parts: 1) **student-furnished materials**; 2) **general laboratory materials**, which are part of the permanent laboratory fixtures; and 3) **supplies**, which should be made available to the students in the laboratory on a per-exercise basis. Also listed are the names and addresses of several vendors of Earth science materials, supplies, and equipment.

Student-furnished materials. In addition to their textbook and class notes, students should purchase and bring the following materials to laboratory sessions. We recommend that a list of these materials be given to each student at the beginning of the course.

calculator	protractor	colored pencils
metric ruler	drawing compass	star chart (optional)

The following can be EITHER purchased by the student OR an adequate number of each should be avail able in the laboratory as general laboratory materials EACH session.

hand lens (2" - 3" diameter)
atlas

General laboratory materials. The following should be part of the permanent laboratory fixtures.

United States or North America physical-political wall map (large, 60" x 60")	lunar globe(s) (12" - 16" diameter)
world physical-political wall map (large, 50" x 90")	floor globe (24" - 30" diameter)
	barometer (mercury)
atlases (or purchased by students)	psychrometer(s) (or hygrometer)
hand lenses (2" - 3" diameter) (or purchased by students)	metric balance(s)
	"bathroom" scale (metric)
student globes (12" diameter)	student telescope(s) (optional)

Supplies. The quantities of the following supplies depend upon the number of students or student stations in the laboratory. However, we recommend that no more than two-to-four students share the same supplies.

mineral specimens	coarse sand, fine sand, soil
streak plate	fossils (optional)
magnet	adding machine paper
glass plate	yardstick
dilute hydrochloric acid	meterstick or metric measuring tape
set of quartz crystals	salt
contact goniometer	salt solutions
binocular microscope	ice
igneous rock specimens	dye
sedimentary rock specimens	rubber band
metamorphic rock specimens	large rubber band
student stereoscope	string
topographic map (local area)	light source
graduated measuring cylinder (100 ml)	clamp for light source
large graduated measuring cylinder	thermometers
beaker (100 ml, graduated)	black and silver containers
small glass funnel	wood splint
ring stand and funnel ring	paper clip
test tubes	nickel coin
cotton	thread
	paper cup

Sources of Earth Science Materials, Supplies, and Equipment

ASC Scientific
2075 Corte del Nogal, Suite 1
Carlesbad, CA 92009
(800) 272-4327 or (619) 431-2655

Ben Meadows Company
3589 Broad Street
P.O. Box 80549
Atlanta (Chamblee), GA 30366
(800) 241-6401 or (404) 455-0907

Carolina Biological Supply Company
2700 York Road
Burlington, NC 27215
(800) 334-5551

D.J. Minerals, Inc.
P.O. Box 761
Butte, MT 59703-0761
(406) 782-7339

Fisher Scientific
Educational Materials Division
4901 West LeMoyne Street
Chicago, IL 60651
(800) 955-1177

Frey Scientific Company
P.O. Box 8081
905 Hickory Lane
Mansfield, OH 44901
(800) 225-FREY

Hammond Incorporated
515 Valley Street
Maplewood, NJ 07040
(800) 526-4953

Hubbard Scientific
1120 Halbleib Road
P.O. Box 760
Chippewa Falls, WI 54729-0760
(800) 323-8368 or (715) 723-4427

Miners, Inc.
P.O. Box 1301
Riggins, Idaho 83549
(800) 824-7452 or (208) 628-3247

NASCO
901 Janesville Avenue
P.O. Box 901
Fort Atkinson, WI 53538-0901
(414) 563-2446

Nystrom
3333 Elston Avenue
Chicago, IL 60618-5898
(800) 621-8086 or (312) 463-1144

Omni Resources, Inc.
2990 Anthony Road
P.O. Box 2096
Burlington, NC 27216
(800) 742-2677 or (916) 227-3748

Rand McNally and Company
P.O. Box 1906
Skokie, IL 60076-9714
(800) 333-0136 or (708) 329-8100

Schoolmasters Science
745 State Circle, Box 1941
Ann Arbor, Michigan 48106
(800) 521-2832

Scott Resources
P.O. Box 2121
Fort Collins, CO 80522
(800) 289-9299 or (303) 484-7445

U.S. Geological Survey
Earth Science Information Center
507 National Center
Reston, VA 22092
(703) 860-6045

Wards Natural Science Establishment
5100 West Henrietta Road
P.O. Box 92912
Rochester, NY 14692-9012
(800) 962-2660 or (716) 359-2502

I hear and I forget,
I see and I remember,
I do and I understand.

-Ancient Proverb

Exercise One
The Study of Minerals

MATERIALS REQUIRED

The following materials are necessary to complete this exercise and should be available in the laboratory. The quantities depend upon the number of students in the laboratory and whether or not students are to work independently or in groups.

mineral specimens
streak plate
magnet
glass plate
binocular microscope

dilute hydrochloric acid (5%)
set of quartz crystals (various sizes)
contact goniometer
crystal growth solution(s)

> **NOTE**: Depending upon the size and quality of the mineral specimens, using a hand lens often helps reduce student frustration.

Recommended mineral specimens: magnetite, pyrite, hematite, graphite, augite, hornblende, smoky quartz, olivine, sphalerite, biotite, potassium feldspar, plagioclase feldspar, milky quartz, calcite, halite, fluorite, muscovite, selenite gypsum, talc, bauxite

TEXTBOOK REFERENCES

Tarbuck and Lutgens, *Earth Science*, 10th edition, 2002. Chapter 1 and Appendix B

Tarbuck and Lutgens, *Earth Science*, 9th edition, 1999. Chapter 1 and Appendix B

Lutgens and Tarbuck, *Foundations of Earth Science*, 3rd edition, 2002. Chapter 1 and Appendix B

Murphy and Nance, *Earth Science Today*, 2001. Chapter 2

Skinner and Porter, *The Blue Planet*, 2nd edition, 1999. Chapter 6

Thompson and Turk, *Earth Science and the Environment*, 2nd edition, 1999. Chapters 42 and 21; Appendix B

PROCEDURES AND STRATEGIES

- The time necessary to complete this exercise can be controlled by the number of mineral specimens assigned for identification. We recommend that the minimum number include those minerals listed above.

- Several methods for presenting the specimens to be identified are possible. 1) Sets for every 2 -4 students can be prepared and placed in trays or plastic containers (we recommend that the individual specimens be numbered so students can check their answers). 2) For those with a limited number of mineral samples, several sets of specimens (each on a numbered card or in a numbered tray) can be placed about the lab.

- Special instructions on the use of a contact goniometer and dilute hydrochloric acid should be given prior to beginning the lab.

- Students often have difficulty with the properties of luster, cleavage, and specific gravity. Discussing and demonstrating these properties prior to beginning the lab is recommended.

- Students often wish to know if their identifications are correct. Therefore, if you have identified individual mineral specimens by numbering them or placing them on a numbered card, we recommend that you fill out a copy of the Mineral Identification Chart, Table 1.3, and posting it after the laboratory session is over.

- In conclusion, throughout the lab period it should be stressed that the goal is to learn how to identify minerals and not simply to "put a name" on them.

NOTES:

ANSWERS TO EXERCISE ONE QUESTIONS

1.-4.   Answers will vary with the mineral specimens provided for identification.

5.   The variety of colors exhibited by different specimens of quartz is primarily the result of trace amounts of chemical constituents (impurities) that can vary from specimen to specimen. For example, the color of rose quartz is due to small amounts of the element titanium, while microscopic fluid pockets (commonly water), called inclusions, produce the white color of milky quartz. Exposure to radiation produces the brown-, gray-, or black-colored quartz, called smoky quartz.

6.   Answers will vary with the mineral specimens provided for identification.

7.   Answers will vary with the mineral specimens provided for identification. However, it should be noted that often a mineral's streak is not the same as its color.

8.   Answers will vary depending on the solutions used. In general, the shape of the crystals should be noted as well as what happens to crystals when they contact one another.

9.   Space limitations during a mineral's formation often restrict crystal growth. However, minerals with imperfect crystal faces still have orderly, internal arrangements of atoms.

10.   Answers will vary with the mineral photograph selected.

11.   The angle between similar, adjacent crystal faces remains the same regardless of the size of the crystal - a property of minerals known as the law of constancy of interfacial angles.

12.   Minerals with one direction of cleavage (basal cleavage) produce thin sheets when cleaved.

13.   a) six planes of cleavage; b) three directions of cleavage; c) the cleavage directions meet at angles other than 90° (rhombohedral cleavage).

14.-16.   Answers will vary with the mineral specimens provided for identification.

17.   talc

18.   The properties and names of the minerals listed on the mineral identification chart will vary with the mineral specimens provided for identification.

19.-20.   Answers will vary with the mineral specimens provided for identification.

> **NOTE**: We recommend that the Mineral Identification Chart, Table 1.3, be filled in and made available for students to verify their mineral identifications.

ANSWERS TO EXERCISE ONE SUMMARY/REPORT PAGE QUESTIONS

1. The procedure for identifying a mineral and arriving at its name involves determining as many of the physical properties of the mineral as possible and then using a mineral identification key to arrive at the name.

2. cleavage; hardness; luster; streak

3. a cube or cubic cleavage

4.-7. Answers will vary with the mineral specimens provided for identification.

8. two directions of cleavage at nearly right angles (90°)

9. the angles are the same

10. Answers will vary with the mineral specimens provided for identification.

11. color: biotite is black, while muscovite is light colored, green-gray

12. specific gravity: chemical composition
cleavage: crystalline structure
color: chemical composition
crystal form: crystalline structure
luster: chemical composition

For Web-based laboratory experiences related to this exercise, make sure you have your students investigate our Website at:

http://www.prenhall.com/earthsciencelab

NOTES:

Exercise Two
Common Rocks

MATERIALS REQUIRED

The following materials are necessary to complete this exercise and should be available in the laboratory. The quantities depend upon the number of students in the laboratory and whether or not students are to work independently or in groups.

igneous rocks	dilute hydrochloric acid
sedimentary rocks	streak plate
metamorphic rocks	glass plate
hand lens or	copper penny
binocular microscope	

Recommended igneous rock specimens: granite, diorite, gabbro, rhyolite, andesite, basalt, porphyritic basalt, obsidian, pumice, tuff

Recommended sedimentary rock specimens: conglomerate, breccia, sandstone, shale, coquina, fossiliferous limestone, chalk, dolostone, chert or flint, rock salt, bituminous coal

Recommended metamorphic rock specimens: slate, phyllite, schist, gneiss, marble, quartzite, anthracite coal

TEXTBOOK REFERENCES

Tarbuck and Lutgens, *Earth Science*, 10th edition, 2002. Chapter 2

Tarbuck and Lutgens, *Earth Science*, 9th edition, 1999. Chapter 2

Lutgens and Tarbuck, *Foundations of Earth Science*, 3rd edition, 2002. Chapter 2

Murphy and Nance, *Earth Science Today*, 2001. Chapter 2

Skinner and Porter, *The Blue Planet*, 2nd edition, 1999. Chapters 6 and 18

Thompson and Turk, *Earth Science and the Environment*, 2nd edition, 1999. Chapter 3

PROCEDURES AND STRATEGIES

- The time required for completing this exercise can be controlled by the number of igneous, sedimentary, and metamorphic rock specimens to be identified.

- Student samples of igneous rocks, sedimentary rocks, and metamorphic rocks should be kept separate so that the different rock types can be compared. Two possible methods for presenting the student specimens are: 1) place each rock type (preferably with each specimen numbered) in separate, labeled trays (or labeled plastic containers) so each group of 2 - 4 students has a complete set; or, 2) for those with a limited number of rock samples, place several separate sets of igneous, sedimentary, and metamorphic rocks on separate numbered cards or in separate numbered trays (i.e. I1, I2,. .S1, S2,. .M1, M2. .) around the laboratory.

- Prior to beginning the laboratory session, a general review of the occurrence, characteristics, textures, and mineral compositions of the three rock types may be beneficial.

- Special instructions should be given on the use of dilute hydrochloric acid before beginning the exercise.

- To assist students in checking their identifications, we recommend that the classification charts for each rock type be filled in and posted after the laboratory session is over. Also, if possible, a set of identified and labeled rocks should be displayed in the laboratory.

- Throughout the laboratory session, it should stressed that the goal of the exercise is to learn how to describe and identify rocks and not to simply "put a name" on them.

NOTES:

ANSWERS TO EXERCISE TWO QUESTIONS

1. igneous rocks and metamorphic rocks

2. metamorphic rocks

3. igneous rocks

4. sedimentary rocks

5. slowly; inside

6. rapidly; on/near the surface

7. phenocrysts; groundmass (or matrix)

8. different crystal sizes; different rates of cooling

9. The sketch showing the arrangement of the magnified mineral crystals in the igneous rock will vary with the specimen selected. However, an interlocking network of crystals should be evident in the diagram.

10. intermediate

11. Although in both examples the mineral crystals are small, the fact that the rocks are composed of different minerals makes their appearances different.

12. Answers will vary with the igneous rock specimens provided.

13. Answers will vary with the sedimentary rock specimens provided.

14. The sketch showing the arrangement of the magnified grains in the sedimentary rock will vary with the specimen selected. However, grains of various shapes and sizes surrounded by finer material should be evident in the diagram. a) fine; b) Specific answers will vary with the specimen selected. However, in general, grains of various shapes and sizes surrounded by finer material should be noted.

15.-16. Answers will vary with the sedimentary rock specimens provided.

17. Students should observe the reaction of the specified sedimentary rock(s) when a small drop of hydrochloric acid is placed on them.

NOTE: In question 17, perhaps both coquina and a coarse, quartz pebble conglomerate with calcite cement can be tested with HCl by the student(s) to illustrate the reaction of grains in contrast to cement.

18. Answers will vary with the sedimentary rock specimens provided.

19. beaches, river channels, sand dunes

20. Sandstone: beach, dunes, shallow sea, delta
     Shale: lagoon, tidal flat, delta, continental slope, deep sea
     Limestone: reef

21. schist

22. gneiss

23. The sketch showing the arrangement of the magnified crystals in the foliated metamorphic rock will vary with the specimen selected. However, alignment of the mineral crystals should be evident in the diagram.

24. Observations will vary with the metamorphic rock specimens provided. However, metamorphic rocks such as quartzite, which are composed primarily of quartz, will scratch glass; while marble, composed primarily of calcite, will not scratch glass but will effervesce with dilute hydrochloric acid.

25. Answers will vary with the metamorphic rock specimens provided.

For Web-based laboratory experiences related to this exercise, make sure you have your students investigate our Website at:

http://www.prenhall.com/earthsciencelab

ANSWERS TO EXERCISE TWO SUMMARY/REPORT PAGE QUESTIONS

1. Igneous rocks: Igneous rocks are the solidified products of magma.

   Sedimentary rocks: Sedimentary rocks form at or near Earth's surface from the accumulated products of weathering, called sediment.

   Metamorphic rocks: Metamorphic rocks form below Earth's surface where high temperatures, pressures, and/or chemical fluids change preexisting rocks without melting them.

2. Foliation - the parallel, linear alignment of mineral crystals perpendicular to compressional forces - occurs in many metamorphic rocks.

3. The name of an igneous rock can be found by first determining its texture and color (an indication of mineral composition), identifying visible mineral grains, and then using an igneous rock identification key.

4. Detrital sedimentary rocks consist of mineral grains or rock fragments derived from the process of mechanical weathering. Chemical sedimentary rocks consist of material that was previously dissolved in water and later precipitated by either inorganic or organic processes.

5. Granite: coarse grained (phaneritic) texture; quartz and potassium feldspar
   Marble: nonfoliated (crystalline) texture; calcite or dolomite
   Sandstone: detrital (medium grain size); usually quartz

6. beach (river channel, delta, or dune)

7. Sedimentary rocks, because they form on Earth's surface and are therefore likely to incorporate the remains of life as fossils.

8. The rate of cooling of the magma determines the size of the mineral crystals in igneous rocks.

9. Since the primary mineral in limestone is calcite, a good chemical test for identifying limestone is to place a small drop of hydrochloric acid on the rock. The mineral calcite will effervesce in acid as carbon dioxide gas is released.

10. The mineral crystals in metamorphic rocks become larger as metamorphism becomes more intense.

11. The most likely metamorphic rock to form from the sedimentary rock limestone is marble.

12. The igneous rock will weather and the products (grains, fragments, and/or dissolved material) may undergo transportation and deposition and become sediment. Lithification of the sediment by cementation, and/or compaction, or precipitation of chemical material will produce either a detrital or chemical a sedimentary rock. Metamorphism by heat, pressure, and/or chemical fluids will transform the sedimentary rock into a metamorphic rock with either a foliated or nonfoliated texture.

13. Answers will vary depending on the rock specimens provided.

NOTES:

Exercise Three
Introduction to Aerial Photographs and Topographic Maps

MATERIALS REQUIRED

The following materials are necessary to complete this exercise and should be available in the laboratory. The quantities depend upon the number of students in the laboratory and whether or not students are to work independently or in groups.

> stereoscope
> topographic map (preferably local)
> United States and world wall maps
> string

> **NOTE**: 1) A hand lens or plastic sheet magnifier can help reduce student frustration when working with topographic maps.
>
> 2) A drafting compass, divider, or piece of string can be useful for measuring distance on a topographic map, especially the length of a river.

TEXTBOOK REFERENCES

Tarbuck and Lutgens, *Earth Science*, 10th edition, 2002. Appendix C

Tarbuck and Lutgens, *Earth Science*, 9th edition, 1999. Appendix C

Lutgens and Tarbuck, *Foundations of Earth Science*, 3rd edition, 2002. Appendix D

Murphy and Nance, *Earth Science Today*, 2001. Appendix D

Skinner and Porter, *The Blue Planet*, 2nd edition, 1999. Appendix D

Thompson and Turk, *Earth Science and the Environment*, 2nd edition, 1999. None

PROCEDURES AND STRATEGIES

- Due to the length of the exercise, some sections may have to be completed outside of the allotted laboratory time or, at the discretion of the instructor, eliminated.

- Some students may not have the capability of stereoscopic vision. Only minor adjustments will be necessary for these students to successfully complete the exercise.

- To complete the entire exercise requires the use of a USGS topographic map that illustrates the Public Land Survey (PLS) system for designating the location of land areas. If you wish to use a map from a region that has not been surveyed with the PLS, then either the exercise will have to be modified or more than one map will be necessary.

- To illustrate different scales, we recommend that samples of the various types of USGS topographic maps be displayed in the laboratory and that students be encouraged to look at them.

- Some students have difficulty working with topographic contours and/or topographic profiles. Often having access to raised relief maps or models helps them understand these concepts.

- If your topographic map collection is extensive, students often find it interesting to look at topographic maps of their home area.

For Web-based laboratory experiences related to this exercise, make sure you have your students investigate our Website at:

http://www.prenhall.com/earthsciencelab

NOTES:

ANSWERS TO EXERCISE
THREE QUESTIONS

1. see completed Figure 3.2

2. see completed Figure 3.2

3. road

4. see completed Figure 3.2

5. see completed Figure 3.2

6 -10. Answers will vary with the map supplied.

11. Highways and roads: red and black
     Buildings: black
     Urban areas: red
     Wooded areas: green
     Water features: blue

12. Topographic map: answers will vary with the map supplied.
     Wall map of the United States: answers will vary with the map supplied.
     World map: answers will vary with the map supplied.
     a) world map
     b) world map

13. 1:24,00: 2000 feet on Earth
     1:63,360: 1 mile on Earth
     1:250,000: nearly 4 miles on Earth

14. Answers will vary with the map supplied.

15. Answers will vary with the map supplied. However, a 15-minute topographic map will cover from 197-281 square miles and the quadrangle area of a 7.5-minute topographic ranges from 49-70 square miles.

16. Answers will vary with the map supplied.

17. Answers will vary with the map supplied (either 7.5 or 15 minutes).

18. Answers will vary with the map supplied.

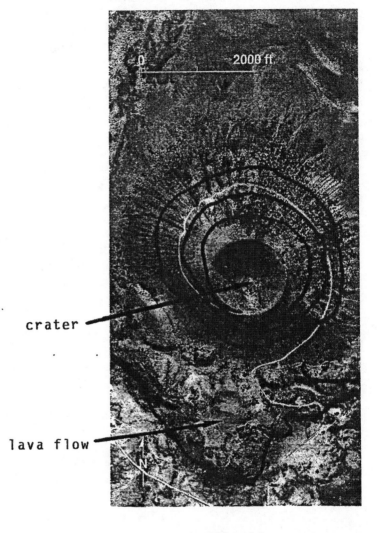

crater

lava flow

Figure 3.2

19.-20. Answers will vary with the map supplied (either 7.5 or 15 minutes).

21. The number of miles or kilometers covered by a minute of longitude becomes increasingly less than the number of miles or kilometers covered by a minute of latitude with increasing distance from the equator. Therefore, since the map covers an equal number of minutes of latitude and longitude, the distance covered by longitude is less than the distance covered by latitude and the map is a rectangle.

22. Answers will vary with the map and feature name supplied.

23. see completed Figure 3.9

24. B) SW 1/4, NE 1/4, Sec. 23, T4S, R2E
    C) NE 1/4, SE 1/4, Sec. 14, T4N, R6E
    D) NW 1/4, NW 1/4, Sec. 31, T5S, R8W

NOTES:

Figure 3.9

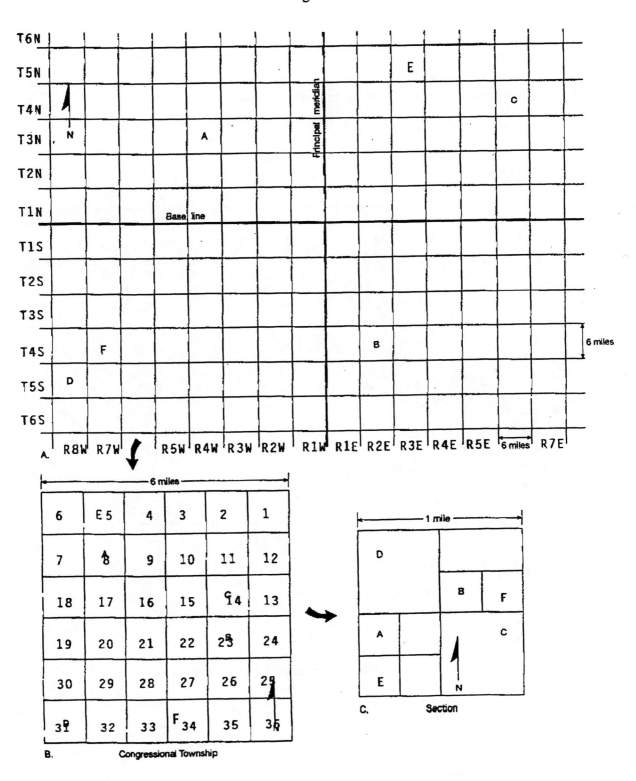

A.

B.   Congressional Township

C.   Section

25. see completed Figure 3.9

26.-28. Answers will vary with the map supplied.

29. Answers will vary with the map and feature name supplied.

30. Students should notice the relations between contour line spacing (as well as the use of hachure marks) and the relief and slope of the various features illustrated on Figure 3.12.

31. Contour interval: 20 feet

32. see completed Figure 3.13

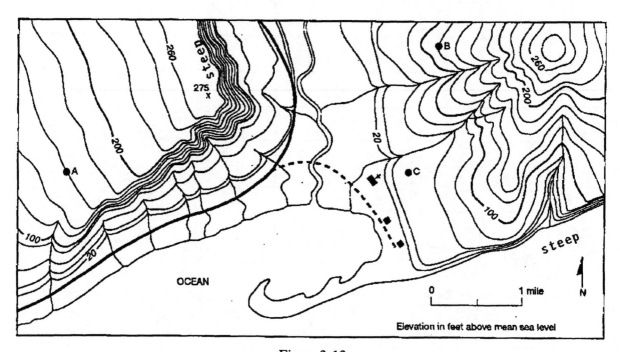

Figure 3.13

33. upstream

34. Point A: 160 feet
     Point B: 120 feet
     Point C: 45 feet (approximate)

35. 12 feet36.Highest elevation (290 feet, approximate) - lowest elevation (0 feet) = total relief (290 feet)

37. slope = 160 feet/mile (approximate)

38.-43. Answers will vary with the map supplied.

44. see completed Figure 3.14

45. south

46. see completed Figure 3.14

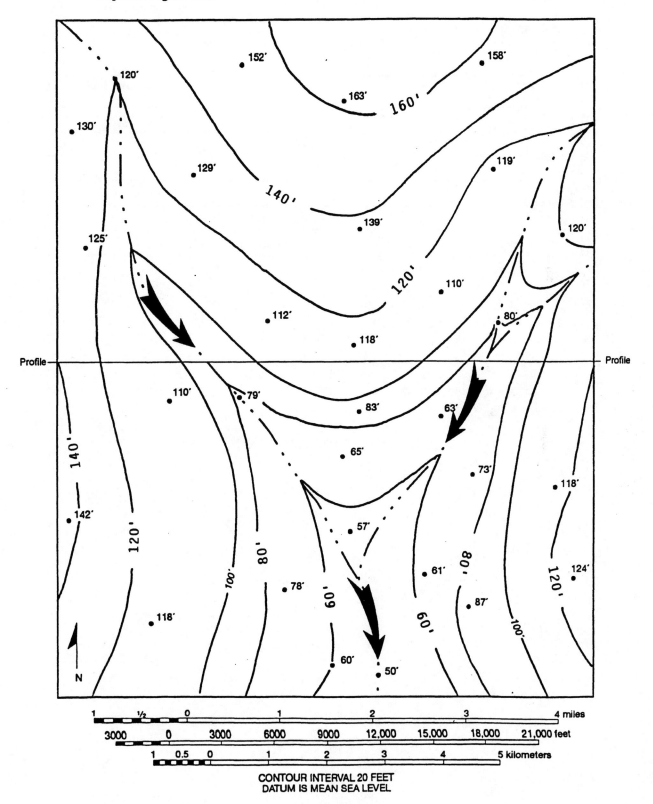

Figure 3.14

47. 10 feet/mile (approximate)

48. see completed Figure 3.16

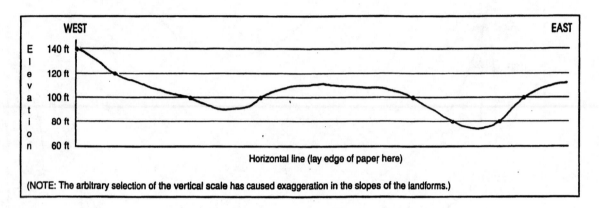

Figure 3.16

For Web-based laboratory experiences related to this exercise, make sure you have your students investigate our Website at:

http://www.prenhall.com/earthsciencelab

NOTES:

ANSWERS TO EXERCISE THREE SUMMARY/REPORT PAGE

1. Stereogram: a stereoscopic aerial photograph composed of two photos of the same feature taken in sequence from an airplane.

   Topographic map: a map that illustrates, to scale, the width, length, and variable height of the land above a datum

   Contour line: a line drawn on a topographic map that connects all points that have equal elevations above or below a datum or reference plane on Earth's surface

   Contour interval: the vertical difference in elevation between adjacent contour lines

   Public Land Survey system: a method of identifying the location of land using a grid system that systematically subdivides the land area

2.-5. Answers will vary with the map supplied.

6. 2,100 feet/mile

7. Answers will vary with the feature selected.

8. 2.8 miles or 4.5 kilometers (4,500 meters)

9. See completed Figure 3.16 (Figure 3.17 will be the same)

10. a) T; b) F; c) F; d) T; e) F

NOTES:

Exercise Four
Shaping Earth's Surface / Running Water and Groundwater

MATERIALS REQUIRED

The following materials are necessary to complete this exercise and should be available in the laboratory. The quantities depend upon the number of students in the laboratory and whether or not students are to work independently or in groups.

graduated measuring cylinder (100 ml)
beaker (100 ml)
small funnel
cotton
coarse sand, fine sand, soil
stereoscope
string

NOTE: 1) A hand lens or plastic sheet magnifier can help reduce student frustration when working with topographic maps.

2) A drafting compass, divider, or piece of string can be useful for measuring distance on a topographic map, especially the length of a river.

TEXTBOOK REFERENCES

Tarbuck and Lutgens, *Earth Science*, 10th edition, 2002. Chapter 4 and Appendix C

Tarbuck and Lutgens, *Earth Science*, 9th edition, 1999. Chapter 4 and Appendix C

Lutgens and Tarbuck, *Foundations of Earth Science*, 3nd edition, 1999. Chapter 3

Murphy and Nance, *Earth Science Today*, 2001. Chapter 10

Skinner and Porter, *The Blue Planet*, 2nd edition, 1999. Chapter 9 and Appendix F

Thompson and Turk, *Earth Science and the Environment*, 2nd edition, 1999. Chapter 4

PROCEDURES AND STRATEGIES

- This exercise involves both a permeability experiment and the use of a stereoscope to view several stereograms; therefore, it may require more time than a single laboratory session to complete. To conserve time, questions 1 through 7 can be assigned as a pre-lab activity and questions 43 through 55 can be completed outside the normal laboratory time.

- While conducting the permeability experiment, students should be instructed to pour the water slowly, but continuously, into the funnel.

- Reading contour lines can be frustrating to students. Therefore, we recommend that a student use a hand lens or sheet magnifier when working with topographic maps.

- Some students may not be capable of stereoscopic vision. However, they still should be able to answer the questions pertaining to the stereograms, especially if they work with a partner who has the ability to see stereoscopic images.

- Since two topographic profiles are to be prepared by the student, a brief review of the procedure (presented in Exercise Three) may be in order.

NOTES:

ANSWERS TO EXERCISE FOUR QUESTIONS

1. oceans

2. 84% (320,000 cubic km/380,000 cubic km x 100)

3. runoff

4. Evaporation: the process of converting a liquid to a gas
   Transpiration: the release of water vapor to the atmosphere by plants
   Runoff: water that flows over the land rather than infiltrating into the ground
   Infiltration: the movement of surface water into rock or soil through cracks or pore spaces

5. as ice in the form of glaciers, or as snow

6. 35 percent (36,000 cubic km/96,000 cubic km x 100)

7. Porosity is the volume of open spaces in rock or soil while permeability is a measure of the material's ability to transmit water.

8. a) coarse sand; b) Materials that consist of large particles (coarse sand) have larger pore spaces than finer materials (soil). Therefore, the water in the centers of the openings in coarse materials is not bound to the particles by molecular attraction (surface tension) and can move more freely through the material. c) Specific answers will vary. However, in general, water will drain faster and less will be held by the coarse sand; while water will drain more slowly through, and more will be retained, by the soil.

9. Highly permeable surface material: high infiltration and low runoff until the material becomes saturated

   Steep slope: high runoff and low infiltration

   Gentle rainfall: infiltration will take place until the material is saturated and then runoff begins

   Dense ground vegetation: will initially slow down runoff so infiltration can take place

10. Initially, moderate infiltration will take place. When the surface of the material is saturated, runoff will dominate.

11. increases

12. The lag time between the time of the rainfall and the time of peak stream discharge becomes less after u rbanization.

13. shorter

14. Stream discharge is greater and occurs quickly in urban areas, which often causes the water to move rapidly through stream channels and overflow their banks.

15. (The area illustrated on the stereogram of the Missouri River is located in the northeast corner of the map, Figure 4.5. It extends from approximately one mile south of the confluence of *Belt Creek* with the *Missouri River* to the north edge of the map.)

16. Approximately 720' of total relief (3,500' - 2780')

17. see completed Figure 4.7

18. see completed Figure 4.7

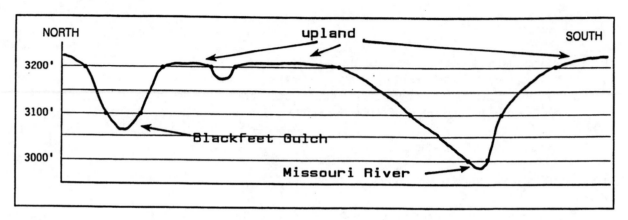

Figure 4.7

19. broad and flat

20. 25% stream valleys; 75% uplands

21. approximately 2,800'

22. eroding

23. They will be eroded and a greater percent of the area will become stream valley.

24. The river is wider up-river from the dams.

25. The upland areas will be eroded and a greater percent of the area will be stream valley with the river more near base level.

26. approximately 640' of total relief (1,880' - 1,240')

27. (On the map, Figure 4.8, the *Genesee River* is flowing from the southeast to the northwest.)

28. approximately 7 feet per mile

29. meanders from valley wall to valley wall

30. relatively narrow ridges

31. Assuming erosion continues in the region without interruption, the areas separating the valleys (divides) will be reduced and more of the region will become floodplain.

32. Approximately 75% of the map area is floodplain.

33.   see completed Figure 4.11

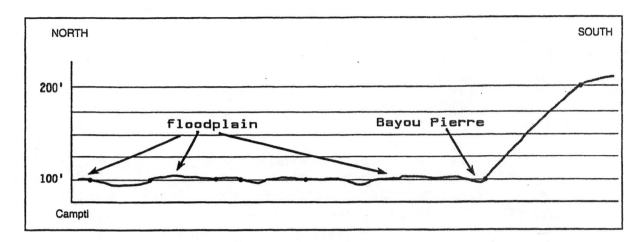

Figure 4.11

34.   Approximately 100' - 120' above ultimate base level

35.   Letter C: oxbow lake, produced when a river cuts off a meander

Letter D: point bar, material deposited by a river on the inside of a meander

Letter E: yazoo tributary, a tributary that flows parallel to the main river on a floodplain because a natural levee is present which prevents it from entering directly into the main river

Letter F: backswamp, a poorly drained area on a floodplain that results when natural levees are present and the slope of the floodplain away from the main channel prevents water from draining into the main channel

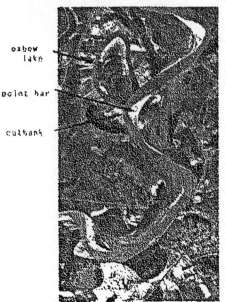

Figure 4.10

36.   see completed Figure 4.10

37. The width of the floodplain is several times wider than the width of the meander belt.

38. lateral erosion

39. The width of the floodplain will increase as lateral erosion by the *Red River* continues.

40. Portage, Montana, map

41. Portage, Montana, map

42. Primarily floodplain: Campti map
    River valleys separated by broad, flat uplands: Portage map
    Most of the area consists of steep slopes: Angelica map
    Greatest number of streams and tributaries: Angelica map (per square mile of area)
    Poorly drained lowland area: Campti map
    Active downcutting by rivers: Portage map
    Surface nearest to base level: Campti map

43. see completed Figure 4.12

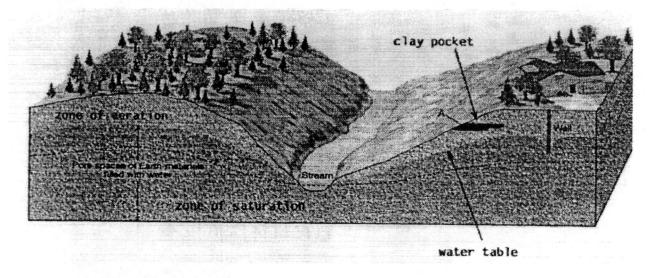

Figure 4.12

44. The shape of the water table conforms closely to the shape of the land surface.

45. The surface of the water in the stream is the water table.

46. The cone of depression is a cone-shaped depression in the water table immediately surrounding a well that forms as water is removed from the zone of saturation by the well. The cone of depression will become larger as more water is pumped from the well.

47. see completed Figure 4.12

48. Water that infiltrates to the level of the clay pocket will, because of the impermeable nature of clay, flow along its surface and produce a spring where the clay pocket intersects the valley wall.

49. The well will no longer penetrate into the zone of saturation and will become dry. The well should have been dug deeper to insure a source of water during the dry season when the water table is lower.

50. sewage and barnyard wastes, among others

51. see completed Figure 4.13

    a. approximately 1.5'/100' (40'/2700') toward the south-southeast

    b. approximately 92' (1130' - 1038')

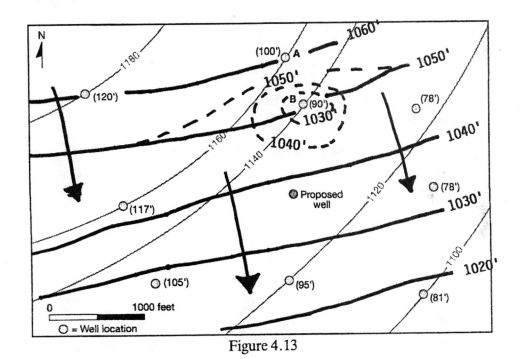

Figure 4.13

52. approximately 1.96 inches (4.98 cm)/day (6000 inches/3065 days)

53. see completed Figure 4.13

54. Ground subsidence closely parallels the fall of the water level in the well.

55. Total ground subsidence = 13 feet
    Total drop in well level = 200 feet

56. 1 foot

57. less

58. Less water was being pumped from the well during this period.

59 (The area illustrated on the Mammoth Cave stereogram is located approximately two miles west of Park City.)

60. The water table is below the depth of the sinkholes.

61. The northern quarter has greater relief and fewer sinkholes.

62. Gardner Creek is being diverted underground through a sinkhole.

63. a) gradually, as carbon dioxide charged rainwater infiltrates and dissolves the underlying rock

   b) suddenly, as a cavern roof collapses

For Web-based laboratory experiences related to this exercise, make sure you have your students investigate our Website at:

http://www.prenhall.com/earthsciencelab

ANSWERS TO EXERCISE FOUR SUMMARY/REPORT PAGE QUESTIONS

1. Precipitation over the land will infiltrate or run off and return to the ocean or evaporation and transpiration from the land will return water vapor to the atmosphere. Water that evaporates from the ocean will end up as precipitation that falls back to the sea or on the land.

2. Subtracting the quantity of run off, evaporation, and transpiration from the total precipitation will yield the quantity of infiltration.

3. Specific answers will vary. However, in general, water will drain faster and less will be held by the coarse sand; while water will drain more slowly through, and more will be retained, by the soil.

4. Urbanization increases the peak discharge of stream flow, shortens the lag time between rainfall and peak stream flow, and shortens the time of total runoff.

5. Because infiltration will be low and runoff high, soil erosion by the flowing surface water will be maximized. Planting a cover crop such as grass or terracing the slope will increase infiltration, reduce runoff, and lessen the soil erosion.

6. Base level: the level below which a stream cannot erode
   Meander: a looplike bend in the course of a river
   Water table: the upper level of the saturated zone of groundwater
   Permeability: a measure of the ability of a material to transmit water
   Aquifer: rock or soil through which groundwater moves easily
   Karst topography: topography consisting of numerous depressions called sinkholes
   Sinkhole: a depression produced in a region where soluble rock has been removed by ground-water

7. Oxbow lake: produced when a river cuts off a meander

   Yazoo tributary: a tributary that flows parallel to the main river on a floodplain because a natural levee is present which prevents it from entering directly into the main river

   Back swamp: a poorly drained area on a floodplain that results when natural levees are present and the slope of the floodplain away from the main channel prevents water from draining into the main channel

8. Factors that should be considered include depth and fluctuation of the water table during the wet and dry seasons as well as permeability within the zone of saturation and contamination of the groundwater.

9. approximately 1.5'/100'

10. approximately 1.96 inches (4.98 cm)/day

11. seek other sources of water such as reservoirs; slow or restrict the rate of withdrawal of ground-water from the aquifer; recharge the aquifer by pumping water from another source into it

12. Sinkholes: depressions produced in a region where soluble rock has been removed by ground-water

    Caves and caverns: underground chambers or series of chambers most commonly produced by the dissolving of limestone by acidic groundwater at or below the water table in the zone of saturation

NOTES:

Exercise Five

Shaping Earth's Surface / Arid and Glacial Landscapes

MATERIALS REQUIRED

The following materials are necessary to complete this exercise and should be available in the laboratory. The quantities depend upon the number of students in the laboratory and whether or not students are to work independently or in groups.

stereoscope
string

> **NOTE:** 1) A hand lens or plastic sheet magnifier can help reduce student frustration when working with topographic maps.
>
> 2) A drafting compass, divider, or piece of string can be useful for measuring distance on a topographic map, especially the length of a river.

TEXTBOOK REFERENCES

Tarbuck and Lutgens, *Earth Science*, 10th edition, 2002. Chapter 5 and Appendix C

Tarbuck and Lutgens, *Earth Science*, 9th edition, 1999. Chapter 5 and Appendix C

Lutgens and Tarbuck, *Foundations of Earth Science*, 3nd edition, 2002. Chapter 4

Skinner and Porter, *The Blue Planet*, 2nd edition, 1999. Chapter 10

Thompson and Turk, *Earth Science and the Environment*, 2nd edition, 1999. Chapters 11 and 12

PROCEDURES AND STRATEGIES

- Most students should be able to complete this exercise within the time allotted for a normal laboratory session.

- Other than requiring a stereoscope to view several stereograms, this exercise could be assigned for completion outside the laboratory as a review of arid and glacial landscapes.

- Reading contour lines can be frustrating to students. Therefore, we recommend that a student use a hand lens or sheet magnifier when working with topographic maps.

- Some students may not be capable of stereoscopic vision. However, they still should be able to answer the questions pertaining to the stereograms, especially if they work with a partner who has the ability to see stereoscopic images.

- Since two topographic profiles are to be prepared by the student, a brief review of the procedure (presented in Exercise Three) may be in order.

ANSWERS TO EXERCISE FIVE QUESTIONS

1. Desert: Southwestern United States (primarily Nevada and Arizona), Baja Peninsula, and north-central Mexico.

   Steppe: Great Plains area (west of the 100°W meridian, including parts of New Mexico, Colorado, Wyoming, Montana, the Dakotas, Nebraska, and Kansas), western and northcentral Mexico.

2. All the statements are misconceptions EXCEPT the that dry regions encompass about 30% of Earth's land surface.

3. (On the topographic map, Figure 5.3, the area illustrated on the Antelope Peak stereogram extends from *Antelope Wash* to approximately four miles north of *Antelope Wash*.)

4. sparse; many

5. approximately 1,300 feet of total relief (2,600' - 1,300')

6. intermittent

7. B

8. (The land surface slopes to the northeast. Therefore, intermittent streams will flow to the north-east as they leave the mountains.)

9. Northeast corner of the map (Since the land surface slopes to the northeast, and the lowest elevations occur in the northeast corner of the map, this is the most likely place for a "possible lake.")

10. Letter C: inselbergs – isolated remnants of mountains characteristic of the late stage of erosion in an arid region.

    Letter D: alluvial fan – A fan-shaped deposit of sediment formed when a stream's slope is abruptly reduced at the base of a mountain.

11. pediment

12. Millions of years ago the Antelope Peak area consisted of block-faulted mountains surrounding an interior basin. The mountains were higher and more extensive than today and less alluvial material filled the basin.

13. Erosion will have further reduced the mountains, alluvial material will fill much of the basin, and more inselbergs may be present.

14. **End** moraines form at the terminus of a glacier.
    Lateral moraines form along the sides of a valley.
    Terminal moraines are end moraines that mark the farthest advance of a glacier.
    Recessional moraines form as the ice front periodically becomes stationary during retreat.
    Ground moraines form as the glacier recedes and lays down a layer of till.
    Medial moraines form when valley glaciers coalesce to form a single ice stream.

15. see completed Figure 5.6

16. see completed Figure 5.6

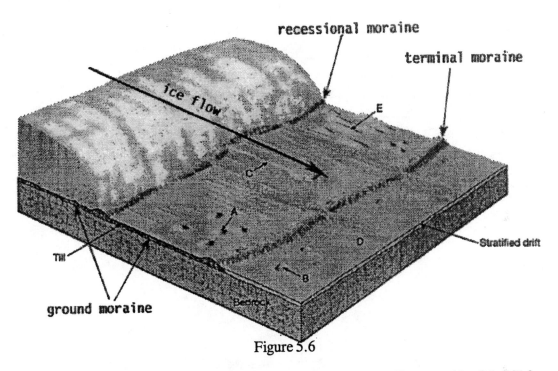

Figure 5.6

17. Drumlin: A streamlined asymmetrical hill composed of glacial till. The steep side of the hill faces the direction from which the ice advanced. Letter: E

Esker: A sinuous ridge composed largely of sand and gravel deposited by a stream flowing in a tunnel beneath a glacier near its terminus. Letter: C

Kame: A steep-sided hill composed of sand and gravel originating when sediment collected in openings in stagnant glacial ice. Letter: A

Kettle: Depressions created when blocks of ice became lodged in glacial deposits and subsequently melted. Letter: B

Outwash plain: A relatively flat, gently sloping plain consisting of materials deposited by melt-water streams in front of the margin of an ice sheet. Letter: D

18. AK, WA, ID, MT, **ND**, SD, **MN, IA**, MO, **WI, IL, MI**, IN, OH, PA, **NY, ME, VT, NH, MA, CT, RI**, NJ

> **NOTE**: In question 18, states shown in **bold** were extensively glaciated by Pleistocene glaciers.

19. (On the topographic map, Figure 5.7, the area illustrated on the stereogram of the Whitewater area extends from just north of *Blue Spring Lake* to approximately four miles south of *Blue Spring Lake*.)

20. higher; more

21. Marshes and swamps in the central and northwest portions of the map indicate that the area is poorly drained.

22. see completed Figure 5.9

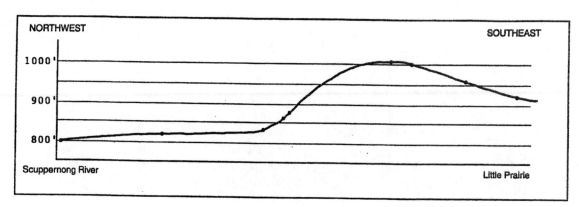

Figure 5.9

23. higher

24. moraine

25. drumlins

26. The steep side of a drumlin faces the direction from which the ice advanced.

27. (The general direction of ice flow would have been from north to south, or slightly southeast.)

28. southeast quarter of the map

29. (Ground moraine would occur in the west half and northeast quarter of the map area.)

30. kettle or kettle hole

31. gravel (perhaps also sand); stratified drift

32. The main valley has become deeper, wider, and "U-shaped."

33. The slopes have become disrupted and much steeper where the tributary streams enter the main valley.

34. Prior to glaciation the ridges were rounded and the stream's gradients were adjusted to the depth of the main valley. Following glaciation, the ridges and peaks are sharp and irregular and the tributaries enter the main valley as waterfalls (hanging valleys).

35. (The large valley glacier is flowing from the top to the bottom of the photograph. A small tributary glacier along the left margin of the photograph is flowing from left to right; while a second tributary glacier, flowing from right to left, is shown in the lower-left corner of the photograph.)

36. a) arete, letter B; b) cirque, letter A; c) lateral moraine, letter D; d) medial moraine, letter C

37. see completed Figure 5.14

38. steep-sided, "U-shaped" valley called a glacial trough

39. Letter B: cirque; Letter C: arete

40. F

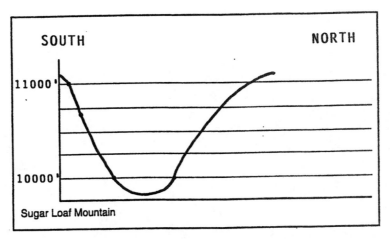

Figure 5.14

41. The feature is a moraine (or end moraine) formed by the accumulation of till at the end of a glacier that at one time flowed down the valley of *Lake Fork*.

42. *Turquoise Lake* has formed because water from *Lake Fork* has been trapped behind the moraine which acts as a dam.

NOTES:

ANSWERS TO EXERCISE FIVE SUMMARY/REPORT PAGE QUESTIONS

1. western and southwestern United States

2. Block-fault mountains have been eroded by streams which have carried and deposited the sediment in an interior basin. The inselbergs and pediment in the area are erosional remnants of the mountains.

3. Letter C: inselbergs; Letter D: an alluvial fan

4. northeast

5. low and intermittent rainfall, high infiltration, high evaporation

6. A moraine would be composed of glacial till, which is characteristically unsorted material consisting of a mixture of clay, silt, sand, and gravel. An esker, on the other hand, would be composed of gravel and sand that has been sorted by water in a river or stream.

7. see sketch

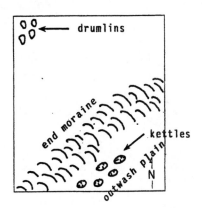

8. Glacial drift, till, stratified drift. moraines, tarns, glacial troughs, cirques, horns, aretes, and scour marks caused by rocks in glaciers as the glaciers moved over bedrock.

9. *Turquoise Lake* has formed because water from *Lake Fork* has been trapped behind the moraine which acts as a dam.

10. Bajada: an accumulation of debris at the base of a block-fault mountains that forms by coalescing of several alluvial fans

    Glacial drift: the general term for any glacial deposit

    End moraine: a ridge of till marking the former position of the front of a glacier

    Horn: a pyramid-shaped peak formed by glacial erosion in three or more cirques surrounding a mountain summit

    Pleistocene epoch: an epoch of the Quaternary period beginning about 1.6 million years ago and ending about 10,000 years ago; best known as the time of extensive continental glaciation

    Inselberg: an isolated mountain remnant characteristic of the late stage of erosion in a block-faulted, arid region with interior drainage

NOTES:

Exercise Six
Determining Geologic Ages

MATERIALS REQUIRED

The following materials are necessary to complete this exercise and should be available in the laboratory. The quantities depend upon the number of students in the laboratory and whether or not students are to work independently or in groups.

fossils and fossil questions (optional)
5 meter length of adding machine paper
meterstick or metric tape measure

TEXTBOOK REFERENCES

Tarbuck and Lutgens, *Earth Science*, 10th edition, 2002. Chapters 10 and 11

Tarbuck and Lutgens, *Earth Science*, 9th edition, 1999. Chapters 10 and 11

Lutgens and Tarbuck, *Foundations of Earth Science*, 3rd edition, 2002. Chapter 8

Murphy and Nance, *Earth Science Today*, 2001. Chapter 3

Skinner and Porter, *The Blue Planet*, 2nd edition, 1999. Chapter 7 and 17

Thompson and Turk, *Earth Science and the Environment*, 2nd edition, 1999. Chapter 4 and Appendix D

PROCEDURES AND STRATEGIES

- The time required to complete this exercise can be controlled by 1) the number of fossils and fossil questions (optional) presented, 2) assigning parts of the exercise to be completed outside the laboratory session, and/or 3) modifying, or eliminating, the time line to be constructed by the students.

- Prior to beginning the laboratory session, a brief review of relative and radiometric dating may be appropriate.

- Since students often have difficulty with geologic block diagrams and cross sections, which are introduced in Exercise Seven, we recommend that at least parts of this exercise be done before Exercise Seven.

- If materials and time permit, we recommend that at least some fossils, or fossil stations with questions, be present in the laboratory – students find the experience of actually working with fossils both interesting and informative.

ANSWERS TO EXERCISE SIX QUESTIONS

1. [OLDEST (first): 8-hearts, 6-diamonds, 3-diamonds, 7-spades, 10-hearts, 5-spades, ace-clubs, 4-hearts, 9-clubs (last) YOUNGEST]

2. No; 2 of clubs could not be "relative" dated. Because the 2 of clubs is not part of the sequence of cards there is no way to determine at what time (first, last, somewhere in the middle) it was laid down.

3. A-D; principle of original horizontality

4. Oldest _E, F, G_ Youngest

5. [In Figure 6.5, the inclusions are the pieces of rock B (a sandstone, illustrated with a light green-dot symbol) found within layer C (a shale, illustrated with a gray-dashed symbol)]

6. B

7. (In Figure 6.4, an angular unconformity separates rock layer E from the inclined rocks below; a disconformity separates rock layer G from rock layer F.)

8. younger

9. younger

10. older

11. After, because the fault cuts through the intrusion.

12. older; younger

13. The fact that there are inclusions of BOTH rock layers B and D in the sill indicates that the sill is more recent than both layers. Since the igneous intrusion H cuts through the sill, the sill is older than H.

14. Answers will vary with the fossils and questions presented.

15. Condition 1: rapid burial
    Condition 2: possession of hard parts

16. Petrification: Photo A
    Cast: Photo C
    Impression: Photo B
    Indirect evidence: Photo D

> **NOTE**: With question 14 we recommend that several numbered fossils (stations) with questions be set around the laboratory. Questions can range from simple observation to determining ages using fossil assemblages.

17. see completed Figure 6.10

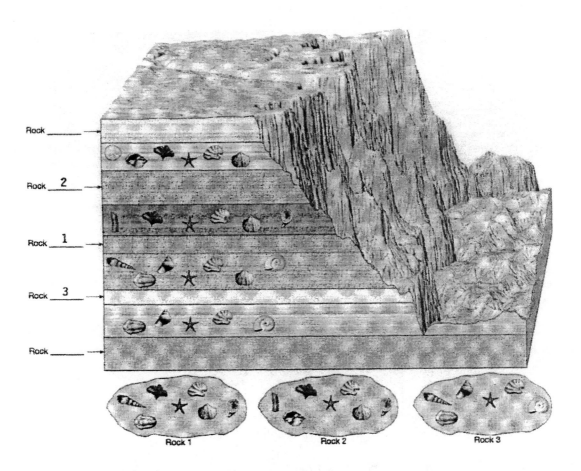

Figure 6.10

18. see completed Figure 6.11

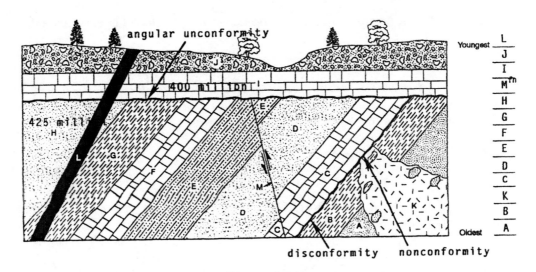

Figure 6.11

19. older; law of superposition

20. older; principle of cross-cutting relationships

21. younger; principle of cross-cutting relationships and inclusions

22. younger

23. see completed Figure 6.11

24. Fault M could have happened at any time after E but before I. Due to the tilting and erosion of the beds through layer H, it can not be determined if the fault extends through beds F, G, and H.

25. One half-life: 1/2
    Two half-lives: 1/4
    Three half-lives: 1/8
    Four half-lives: 1/16

26. One half-life: 5.0 grams
    Four half-lives: 0.63 grams

27. 400 million years

28. 1,800 million years (3 half-lives x 600 million years per half-life)

29. 1/2 parent and 1/2 daughter: Age = 100 million years
    1/8 parent and 7/8 daughter: Age = 300 million years
    1/32 parent and 31/32 daughter: Age = 500 million years

30. a) half; b) one half-life; c) 425 million years; see completed Figure 6.11

31. see completed Figure 611

32. 25 million years (approximate); the difference between the ages of layers H and I

33. older; cross-cutting relationship indicates that fault M is older than layer I

34. Intrusion L formed more recently than 400 million years ago.

35. All the rock layers are **older** than **425** million years.

36. (Time line to be constructed by student(s) using the indicated scale and Figure 6.13.)

> With question 36, instructors may wish to add more events to those listed in Figure 6.13.

37. approximately 88 percent, or 7/8 (4,030 million years, the time represented by the Precambrian eon, divided by 4,600 million years, the age of Earth).

38. Approximately 570 million years age was selected because it marks the appearance of the first life-forms with hard parts. Because hard parts greatly enhances an organism's chances of being preserved as part of the fossil record, our knowledge of life's diversification improves greatly from this point onward.

39. Because the Cenozoic is the most recent era, the fossil record is clearer and more accessible for determining additional subdivisions with reasonable accuracy.

40. 920,000 times longer (4,600 million years divided by 5,000 years)

41. Approximately 1/10 (.095) of geologic time. (438 million years divided by 4,600 million years)

NOTES:

ANSWERS TO EXERCISE SIX SUMMARY/REPORT PAGE QUESTIONS

1. See completed Figure 6.14 (NOTE: Fault J could have happened at any time after C but before F. However, the absence of any unconformities between C and E suggests that J occurred after E.)

2. a) disconformity; b) law of superposition; c) cross-cutting relationships; d) the igneous intrusion cuts through the fault; e) between 160 and 150 million years; f) Layer G: 75 million years; Layer F: 150 million years; g) From 150 to 75 million years

3. Oldest _A, B, K, C, D, E, F, G, H, M, I, J, L_ Youngest

4. Phanerozoic eon: 0.12 of geologic time (540 million years divided by 4,500 million years)
   Precambrian eon: 0.88 of geologic time (3,9600 million years divided by 4,500 million years)

5. 4,500 meters (4,500,000 millimeters, 4,500 million years divided by 1,000 years per millimeter)

6. The sedimentary rock layers were deposited with the oldest at the bottom (superposition).
   The igneous intrusions formed more recently (cross-cutting). (From the evidence provided, it can not be determined if both sills are the same age, or one is more recent than the other.)

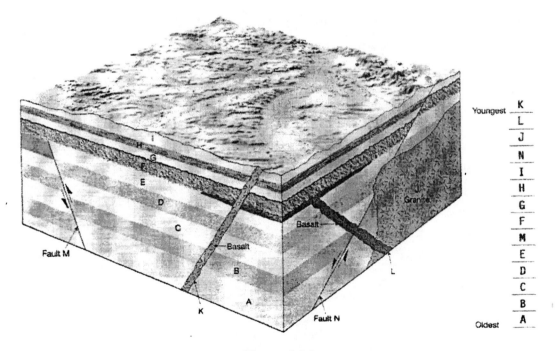

Figure 6.14

NOTES:

Exercise Seven
Geologic Maps and Structures

MATERIALS REQUIRED

The following materials are necessary to complete this exercise and should be available in the laboratory. The quantities depend upon the number of students in the laboratory and whether or not students are to work independently or in groups.

No instructor supplied materials needed

TEXTBOOK REFERENCES

Tarbuck and Lutgens, *Earth Science*, 10th edition, 2002. Chapters 9

Tarbuck and Lutgens, *Earth Science*, 9th edition, 1999. Chapter 9

Lutgens and Tarbuck, *Foundations of Earth Science*, 3rd edition, 2002. Chapter 6

Murphy and Nance, *Earth Science Today*, 2001. Chapter 3 and 6

Skinner and Porter, *The Blue Planet*, 2nd edition, 1999. Chapter 7

Thompson and Turk, *Earth Science and the Environment*, 2nd edition, 1999. Chapter 8 and Appendix D

PROCEDURES AND STRATEGIES

- In its entirety, the exercise covers quite a bit of material. Therefore, since no instructor supplied materials are necessary to work the exercise, parts, or all, of it could be assigned for completion outside of the laboratory session.

- Many students have difficulty understanding strike and dip as well as visualizing geologic block diagrams and/or cross sections. We recommend a brief discussion of these, perhaps with examples, before beginning the exercise.

- Working through some of the figures step-by-step with the students may be helpful.

- For this exercise, it would be best to instruct the students to "sketch" rather than attempt to "construct" the geologic block diagrams and cross sections.

- A brief discussion of geologic maps and map explanations, perhaps using Figures 7.24 and 7.25, may be beneficial.

- Remember to inform the students that the goal is not to become a "master" draftsperson, but rather to understand the techniques used by geologists to map and interpret geologic structures.

ANSWERS TO EXERCISE SEVEN QUESTIONS

1. see completed Figure 7.5

2. see completed Figure 7.7

3. see completed Figure 7.8

4. see completed Figure 7.9

5. see completed Figure 7.15

6. Anticline: Oldest _1, 2, 3, 4, 5_ Youngest
   Syncline: Oldest _1, 2, 3, 4, 5_ Youngest

7. axial plane

8. see completed Figure 7.15

9. away

10. toward

11. asymmetrical; symmetrical

12. nonplunging

13. see completed Figure 7.15

14. a) younger; b) older

15. see completed Figure 7.16

16. see completed Figures 7.18
    Eroded dome: rocks dip away from the center; oldest rocks are exposed in the center
    Eroded basin: rocks dip toward the center; youngest rocks in the center

17. see completed Figure 7.20

18. see completed Figure 7.20: a) youngest; b) oldest

19. see completed Figure 7.21

20. see completed Figure 7.23

21. 1:31,250; one inch equals approximately 0.5 mile

22. Youngest: Phosphoria formation; Age: 245 - 286 million years (Permian)
    Oldest: Greyson shale; Age: 570 - 2000 million years (upper Precambrian)

23. [oldest sedimentary rocks (Precambrian, Greyson shale, light gray color, pCg symbol) occur along the south-central edge of the map and extend to the northeast; youngest sedimentary rocks shown on the "Explanation" (Permian, Phosphoria formation, gray-green color, Pp/PPq symbol) occur near the north west corner] NOTE: In the extreme northwest corner of the map, the rocks shown in yellow with light green stripes, Kk, (Cretaceous period) are younger but they are not indicated on the "Explanation."

24. younger (the intrusive rocks are of Tertiary and Cretaceous ages)

25. (In the central and western portion of the map the rocks are dipping toward the west and northwest, in the eastern third of the map the rocks are dipping toward the east and northeast); a) northwest; b) east

26. 35° - 60°

27. [The axial plane of the large geologic structure extends from the center of the south edge of the map (southeast corner of section 23) to the northeast corner of the map.]

28. anticline; 1) the rock layers dip away from the axial plane; 2) the oldest exposed rocks are at the center of the structure, along the axial plane

29. (If the direction of dip of the faults in section 14 is toward the southwest, then normal faults occur in the center of section 14 and reverse faults are found along the north and south borders of the section.)

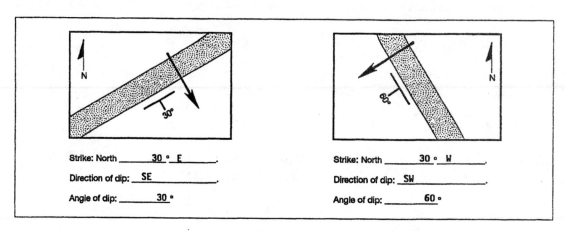

Strike: North ___30___°_E___.

Direction of dip: __SE__.

Angle of dip: ___30___°

Strike: North ___30___°__W___.

Direction of dip: __SW__.

Angle of dip: ___60___°

Figure 7.5

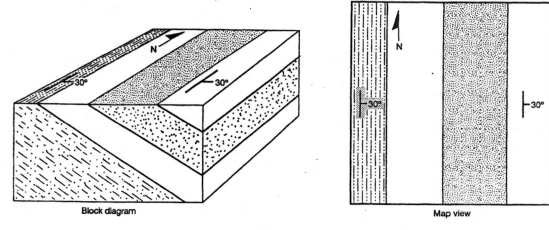

Block diagram

N

30°

30°

Map view

N

30°

30°

Figure 7.7

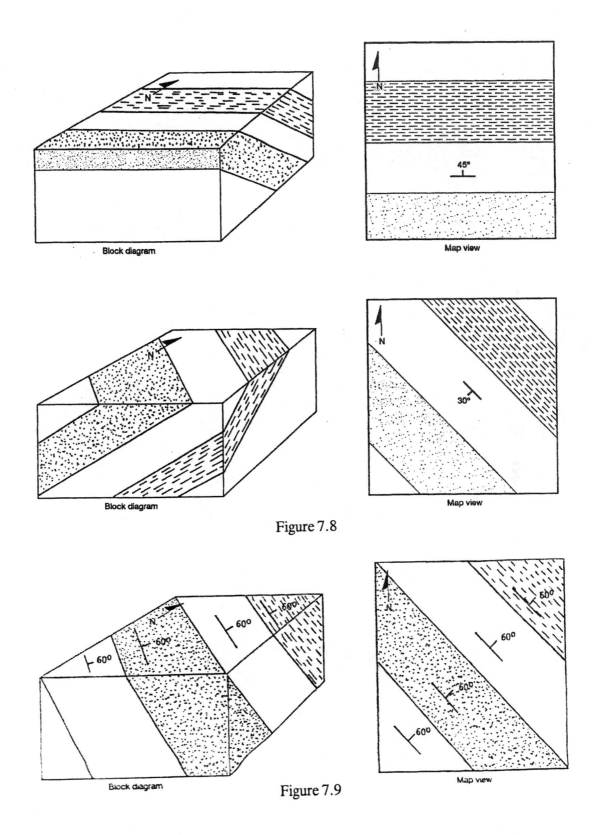

Block diagram

Map view

Block diagram

Map view

Figure 7.8

Block diagram

Figure 7.9

Map view

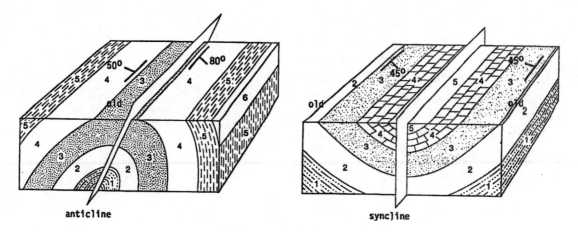

Figure 7.15

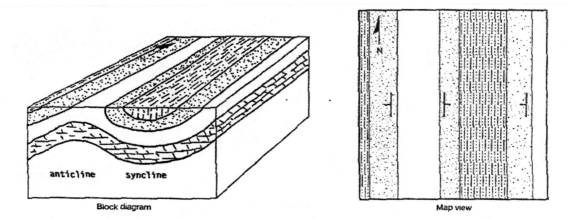

Figure 7.16

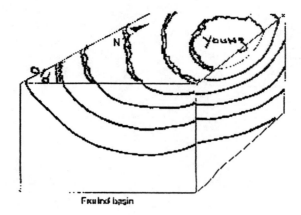

Figure 7.18

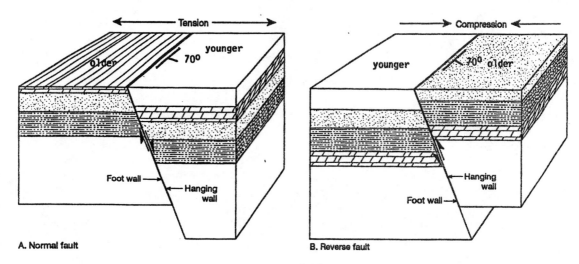

Figure 7.20

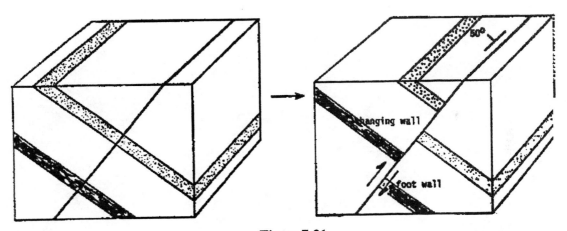

Figure 7.21

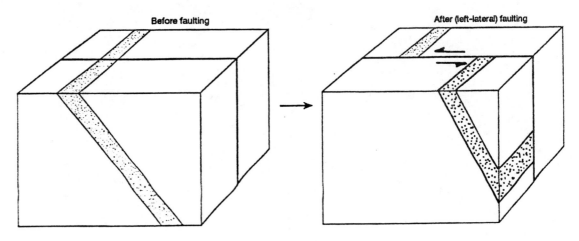

Figure 7.23

NOTES:

ANSWERS TO EXERCISE SEVEN SUMMARY/REPORT PAGE QUESTIONS

1. Strike: North 25° East
   Angle of dip: 30°
   Direction of dip: northwest

2. See completed Figure 7.26

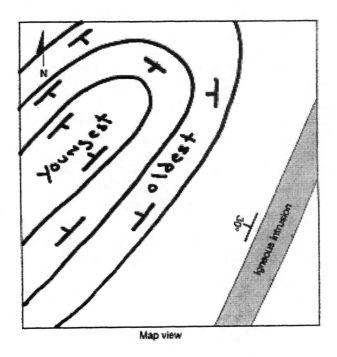

Figure 7.26

3. anticline; 1) the rock layers dip away from the axial plane; 2) the oldest exposed rocks are at the center of the structure, along the axial plane

4. anticline and reverse fault

5. Compression

6. Strike: the compass direction of the line produced by the intersection of an inclined rock layer or fault with a horizontal plane at the surface

    Dip: angle of inclination of the surface of the rock unit or fault from the horizontal plane

    Symmetrical anticline: a structure where the rock layers fold upward and the limbs on both sides of the axial plane are mirror images of each other and diverge at the same angle

    Normal fault: a fault in which the rock above the fault plane (hanging wall) has moved down relative to the rock below the fault plane (footwall)

    Axial plane: an imaginary plane drawn through the long axis of a fold that divides it as equally as possible into two halves

    Left-lateral fault: a strike-slip fault where the side opposite from the side where you are standing has been displaced to the left relative to your position

7. see completed Figure 7.27 below

8. The youngest rocks are located at the axial plane (the center of the structure) in an eroded syncline.

9. The fault illustrated is a normal fault (hanging wall (left) has moved down relative to the foot wall). Tensional forces most likely produced the fault.

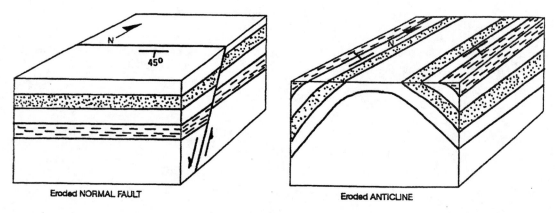

Figure 7.27

Exercise Eight
Earthquakes and Earth's Interior

MATERIALS REQUIRED

The following materials are necessary to complete this exercise and should be available in the laboratory. The quantities depend upon the number of students in the laboratory and whether or not students are to work independently or in groups.

atlas or wall map

TEXTBOOK REFERENCES

Tarbuck and Lutgens, *Earth Science*, 10th edition, 2002. Chapter 6

Tarbuck and Lutgens, *Earth Science*, 9th edition, 1999. Chapter 6

Lutgens and Tarbuck, *Foundations of Earth Science*, 3rd edition, 2002. Chapter 6

Murphy and Nance, *Earth Science Today*, 2001. Chapter 7

Skinner and Porter, *The Blue Planet*, 2nd edition, 1999. Chapter 5

Thompson and Turk, *Earth Science and the Environment*, 2nd edition, 1999. Chapter 6

PROCEDURES AND STRATEGIES

- The exercise is a rather straight forward, step-by-step, approach to earthquakes and Earth's interior and most students should be able to complete it within the time allotted for a normal laboratory session.

- Since the only additional materials required to complete the exercise are an atlas or North American map, this exercise could also be done outside the laboratory as homework or review.

- Some discussion concerning the use of the travel-time graph, Figure 8.4, may be appropriate before beginning the exercise.

- If you have access to a seismograph, either actual or simplified, a demonstration often helps students understand the technique for recording seismograms.

ANSWERS TO EXERCISE EIGHT QUESTIONS

1. 11

2. Five

3. Seven

4. 5

5. 30

6. greater

7. increases

8. 1000 miles: 3.25 minutes difference
   2400 km: 4.20 minutes difference
   3000 miles: 6.50 minutes difference

9. 2100 miles

10. 7 (approximate)

11. 10:32 PM (approximate)

12. Table 8.1

	New York	Seattle	Mexico City
Elapsed time between first P and first S waves	5.5 min.	4 min.	3.5 min.
Distance from epicenter in miles	2400 mi.	1400 mi.	1200 mi.

13. see completed Figure 8.7

14. see completed Figure 8.7

15. 28°N latitude and 112°30'W longitude

16. 8:54 UTC (7 minutes difference between the actual time of the earthquake and when it was recorded in New York)

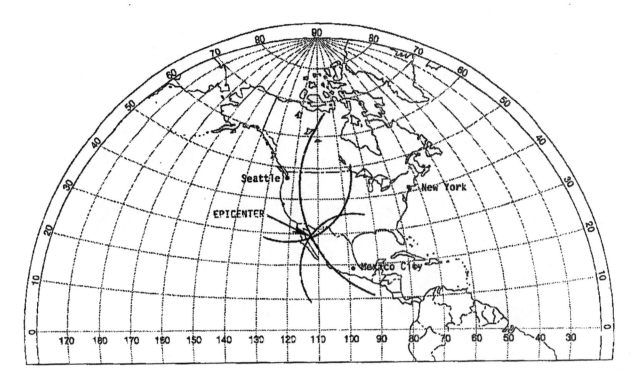

Figure 8.7

17. Belt 1: near the outer edge of the Pacific Ocean, known as the circum-Pacific belt

Belt 2: the mountainous regions that flank the Mediterranean Sea and continue through Iran and on past the Himalayan complex

Belt 3: through the world's oceans and coinciding with the oceanic ridge system

18. There is a close correlation between the location of earthquake epicenters and plate boundaries.

19. 100; a) lithosphere; b) P wave velocity: 7-8 km/sec, S wave velocity: 4-4.5 km/sec; c) increases; d) 1. continental crust, felsic (granitic) rocks, and 2. oceanic crust, basaltic composition

20. 700; a) asthenosphere; b) decreases; c) partially molten

21. 2885 kilometers; a) mantle; b) both S and P waves can travel through the mantle; c) Ultramafic rocks such as peridotite are thought to make up the mantle and provide lava for oceanic erup-tions.

22. 5100; a) outer core; b) S waves do not propagate through the zone; therefore, at least a portion of the zone is liquid; c) decreases

23. inner core; a) 5100 km to the center of Earth; b) the velocity of P waves increases, sug-gesting that the inner core is solid; c) the core of Earth is thought to be mainly iron and nickel

24. see completed Figure 8.9

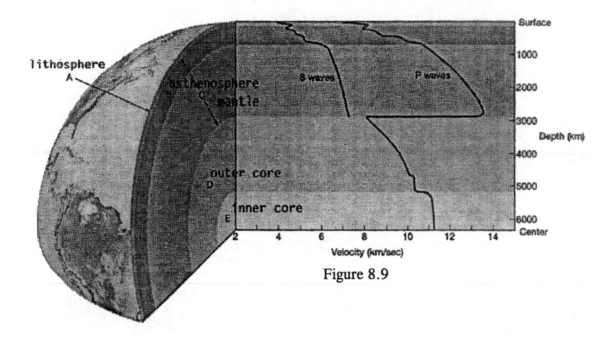

Figure 8.9

25. see completed Figure 8.10

26. changes

27. greater

28. 1400

29. 1400°C/100 km, 14°C/km

30. see completed Figure 8.10

31. 25 km within Earth (approximate)
     (At this depth, the internal temperature
     of Earth is approximately the same as
     the melting temperature for wet granite.)

32. has not; solid

33. 100 km; partly melted

34. asthenosphere

35. One model proposed by scientists is that, because the asthenosphere is partly molten, heat from within Earth may cause convection currents to form in the mantle. These convection cells within the asthenosphere act like "conveyor belts" and drag the rigid lithosphere along as the material moves.

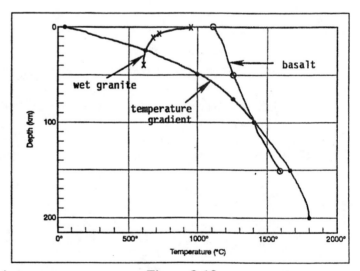

Figure 8.10

36. 600 kilometers

37. nearly along a line

38. see completed Figure 8.11

39. see completed Figure 8.11

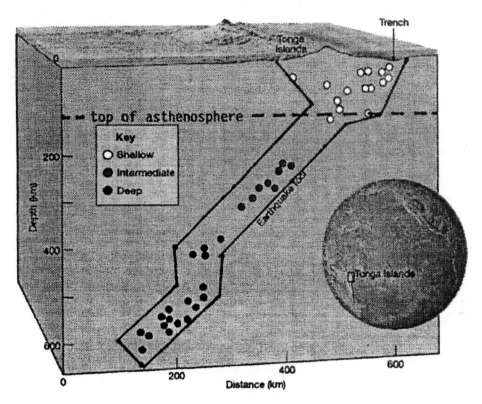

Figure 8.11

40. Earthquakes occur in solid, rigid material. Near Tonga, earthquake foci are recorded along a relatively narrow zone at increasing depths well into the asthenosphere, which is partly molten, or "plastic" material. Therefore, the most likely explanation is that a portion of the solid lithosphere is descending into the "plastic" mantle and generating earthquakes as it heats, breaks up, and is assimilated.

NOTES:

ANSWERS TO EXERCISE EIGHT SUMMARY/REPORT PAGE QUESTIONS

1.

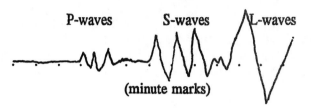

P-waves   S-waves   L-waves

(minute marks)

2. approximately 2100 miles

3. The epicenter of on earthquake is located by using the difference in arrival times of the P and S waves from recordings of the same earthquake made at a minimum of three different locations. Each place determines their distance from the epicenter using a travel-time graph. A circle with a radius corresponding to the distance from the epicenter is drawn around each place. The lo-cation where all three circles intersect is the epicenter of the earthquake.

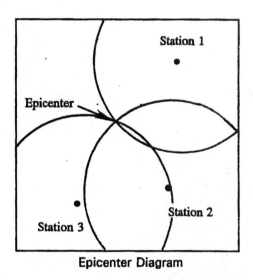

Epicenter Diagram

4. Belt 1: near the outer edge of the Pacific Ocean, known as the circum-Pacific belt

   Belt 2: the mountainous regions that flank the Mediterranean Sea and continue through Iran and on past the Himalayan complex

   Belt 3: through the world's oceans and coinciding with the oceanic ridge system

5. partly melted

6. they are not transmitted

7. Mantle: depth from below the crust (5-40 km) to 2885 km; Composition: ultramafic rocks such as peridotite

   Outer core: depth from 2885 km to 5155 km; Composition: iron and nickel

8. 25 kilometers (approximate)

9. Earthquakes occur in solid, rigid material. Near Tonga, earthquake foci are recorded along a relatively narrow zone at increasing depths well into the asthenosphere, which is partly molten, or "plastic" material. Therefore, the most likely explanation is that a portion of the solid lithosphere is descending into the "plastic" mantle and generating earthquakes as it heats, breaks up, and is assimilated.

10. Earthquake focus: the zone within Earth where rock displacement produces an earthquake

    Earthquake epicenter: the location on Earth's surface that lies directly above the focus of an earthquake

    Seismogram: the record of an earthquake made by a seismograph

    Asthenosphere: a subdivision of the mantle situated below the lithosphere from a depth of about 100 km to as deep as 700 km.

    Geothermal gradient: the increase in the temperature of Earth with depth

    Lithosphere: the rigid outer zone of Earth which includes the crust and part of the upper mantle

11. See completed Figure 8.12

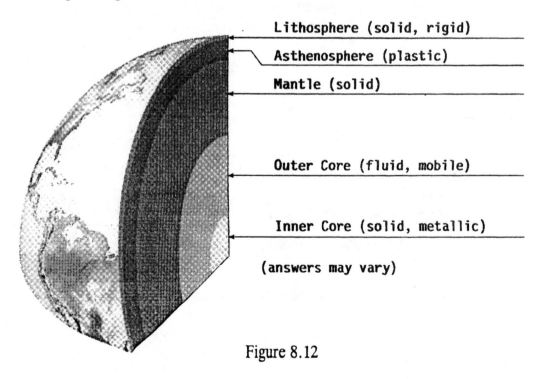

Lithosphere (solid, rigid)

Asthenosphere (plastic)

Mantle (solid)

Outer Core (fluid, mobile)

Inner Core (solid, metallic)

(answers may vary)

Figure 8.12

Exercise Nine
Introduction to Oceanography

MATERIALS REQUIRED

The following materials are necessary to complete this exercise and should be available in the laboratory. The quantities depend upon the number of students in the laboratory and whether or not students are to work independently or in groups.

measuring cylinder
  (100 ml, clear, pyrex
  or plastic)
test tubes
salt
salt solutions

world wall map,
  globe or atlas
ice
dye
rubber band
beaker

NOTE: The quantity of each glassware item necessary to conduct the exercise will depend upon whether or not the experiments are to be done by individual students, in groups, or as demonstrations.

TEXTBOOK REFERENCES

Tarbuck and Lutgens, *Earth Science*, 10th edition, 2002. Chapters 12 and 13

Tarbuck and Lutgens, *Earth Science*, 9th edition, 1999. Chapter 2

Lutgens and Tarbuck, *Foundations of Earth Science*, 3nd edition, 2002. Chapter 9

Murphy and Nance, *Earth Science Today*, 2001. Chapter 8

Skinner and Porter, *The Blue Planet*, 2nd edition, 1999. Chapter 11

Thompson and Turk, *Earth Science and the Environment*, 2nd edition, 1999. Chapters 13 and 14

PROCEDURES AND STRATEGIES

- Two in-lab experiments, salinity-density and temperature-density, are included with this exercise. Should you decide to do both experiments during the lab period, to conserve time, we recommend that questions 1 through 12, which involve locating water bodies on a world map and ocean floor features on a map of the North Atlantic Ocean basin, be assigned as pre-lab activities.

- Depending on the quantities of glassware and materials available, students should work in groups of two to six to conduct the experiments.

- In labs with very limited supplies, we recommend that, at the very least, the experiments be done as demonstrations and that students use the information to complete the appropriate questions.

- Question 18 offers a good opportunity to review and discuss the factors that control ocean water salinities.

ANSWERS TO EXERCISE NINE QUESTIONS

1. (Students who have completed Exercise Nine and HAVE NOT done Exercise Twenty-one should see ALTERNATE completed Figure 21.8)

2. 71% (360 million square kilometers divided by 510 million square kilometers, x 100)

3. 29%

4. "Water" hemisphere: Southern Hemisphere
   "Land" hemisphere: Northern Hemisphere

5. 40°: 50% ocean (Northern Hemisphere); 95% ocean (Southern Hemisphere)
   60°: 40% ocean (Northern Hemisphere); 100% ocean (Southern Hemisphere)
   a) more narrow
   b) increases

6. Pacific

7. (Students are to label one or more examples of a continental shelf on Figure 9.2)

   Continental shelf: gently sloping submerged portion of the continental margin extending from the shoreline to the continental slope

   a) approximately 200 feet (the depth ranges from 0 on the shore to over 400 feet at the seaward edge): b) narrow along the west coast (with the exception of Alaska) and wider along the east and gulf coasts

8. (Students are to label one or more examples of a continental slope on Figure 9.2)
   Continental slope: seaward edge of the continental shelf with a steep gradient that leads to the deep-ocean floor

   a) Most available information seems to favor the view that submarine canyons have been excavated at least in part by turbidity currents. (Students are to label at least two examples of a submarine canyon on Figure 9.2)

9. (Students are to label one or more examples of an abyssal plain on Figure 9.2)

   Abyssal plain: very level area of the deep-ocean floor, usually lying at the foot of the continental rise

   a) flat; b) thick accumulations of sediments transported far out to sea by turbidity currents that were deposited atop the low, rough portions of the ocean floor

10. (Students are to label one or more examples of a seamount on Figure 9.2)

    Seamount: isolated volcanic peak that rises at least 1000 meters above the deep-ocean floor

11. (Students are to label an example of a deep-ocean trench on Figure 9.2)

    Deep-ocean trench: narrow, elongated depression on the floor of the ocean

    a) 8400 meters (28,000 feet); b) (Answers will vary depending on the trenches selected.) Tonga trench, 22°S and 175°W, 10,000 meters; Mariana trench, 12°N and 145°E, 10,000 meters; Kuril trench, 45°N and 153°E, 10,000 meters

12. (Students are to label the mid-ocean ridge on Figure 9.2)

Mid-ocean ridge: continuous mountain ridge on the floor of all the major ocean basins that varies in width from 500 to 5000 kilometers

a) extends beneath the continent; b) approximately 3000 meters

Step 2. Observations: the saltwater sinks to the bottom of the cylinder

13. a) the density of saltwater increases as its salinity is increased b) Answers will vary depending on which solution has been made most dense (saline). However, the most dense (saline) will travel faster.

14. see completed Figure 9.4 Higher surface salinities occur at approximately 20°-30° latitudes in both hemispheres.

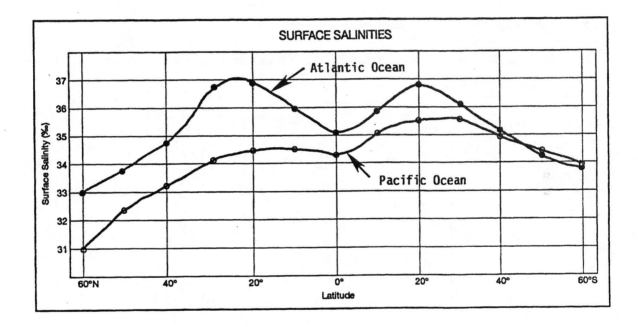

Figure 9.4

15. Precipitation, which dilutes the seawater and lowers the concentration of salt, and evaporation which removes water and increases the concentration.

16. Precipitation has lowered the concentration in equatorial water while evaporation in subtropical regions has increased the concentration.

17. Atlantic

18. Several different answers may be given by the student. For example: differences in the two oceans between the balance of precipitation and evaporation; more salts added to the Atlantic by runoff and less removed by precipitation; salts added to the Atlantic from the enclosed Caribbean and Mediterranean; or freezing of sea water in the North Atlantic.

[According to Dietrich (Dietrich, Gunther. *General Oceanography*, John Wiley & Sons, New York, 1963) among the reasons that the salinity of the Atlantic, particularly the North Atlantic, is higher than that of the Pacific may also be listed the following: 1) the North Atlantic tradewind belt extends into the Pacific Ocean across the Isthmus of Panama and contributes high precipitation in the Gulf of Panama region; 2) the west winds from the Pacific Ocean release their moisture over the Cordilleras, returning water to the Pacific. No comparable mountain barriers exist in Europe and Africa, and consequently the influences of water vapor of Atlantic origin are much more widespread; 3) the North Pacific lacks the enclosed seas, such as the Mediterranean and Caribbean, which contribute highly saline waters at inter mediate depths to the Atlantic.]

19. decreases; increases

20. evaporation at the surface causing higher concentrations

21. The halocline is the zone of rapid salinity change below the surface water. see completed Figure 9.5

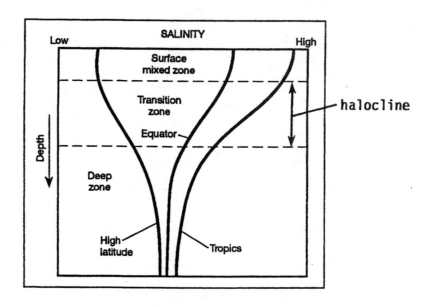

Figure 9.5

22. remains fairly constant

Step 3. Observations: the hot water remains on the surface of the cooler water in the cylinder

Step 5. Observations: the cold water sinks to the bottom of the warmer water in the cylinder

23. a) Cold water has a greater density than warm water and therefore sinks to the bottom of cylinder. b) cold

24. see completed Figure 9.7; (warm; low); (cool; high)

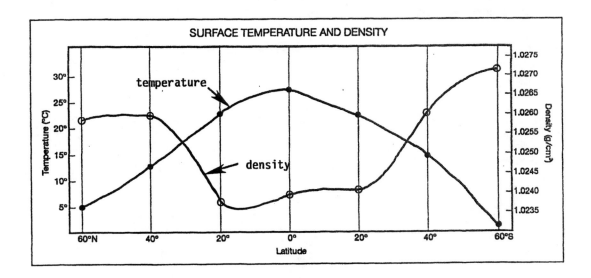

Figure 9.7

25. cooler surface temperatures

26. Although surface salinities are greatest at about latitudes 30°N and 30°S, surface densities are greatest at higher latitudes which indicates that temperature is more of a controlling factor of density than salinity.

27. low; The temperature of deep-ocean water is fairly constant over the Earth. Because of the mechanism by which Earth is heated, surface water temperatures are higher at low latitudes and therefore the temperature of ocean water decreases with depth most rapidly at these latitudes.

28. The thermocline is the layer of rapid temperature change below the surface water. It marks the transition between the warm surface layer and cold water below. see completed Figure 9.8

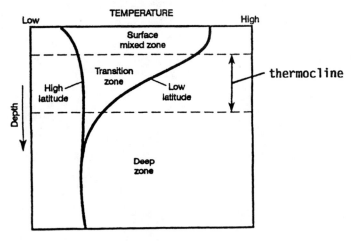

Figure 9.8

29. remains fairly constant

For Web-based laboratory experiences related to this exercise, make sure you have your students investigate our Website at:

http://www.prenhall.com/earthsciencelab

NOTES:

ANSWERS TO EXERCISE NINE SUMMARY/REPORT PAGE QUESTIONS

1. Mediterranean Sea: 36°N and 18°E
   Sea of Japan: 39°N and 134°E
   Indian Ocean: 20°S and 80°E

2. In the Northern Hemisphere, the "land" hemisphere, the continents become wider and the oceans more narrow from the equator to the pole. In the Southern Hemisphere, the "water" hemisphere, the continents become more narrow and the oceans wider from the equator to the pole.

3. see completed Figure 9.9

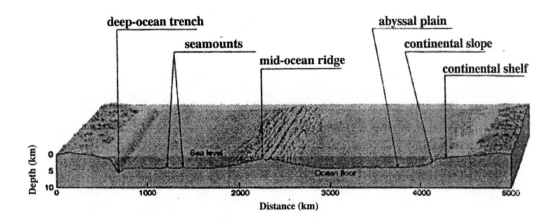

Figure 9.9

4. Answers will vary. Tonga trench, 10,000 meters; Mariana trench, 10,000 meters

5. a) higher; b) higher (to 4°C, at temperatures below this the density decreases); c) subtropical; d) Temperature; e) Cold, high (to 4°C); f) polar, most

6. higher evaporation rates at these latitudes increase the concentration of surface salts

7. (the answer depends upon which solution, A or B, was prepared with the highest salinity)

8. Salinity: At low latitudes, salinity decreases with depth most rapidly in the halocline. Below the halocline salinity remains fairly constant.

   Temperature: At low latitudes, temperature decreases with depth most rapidly in the thermocline. Below the thermocline temperature remains fairly constant.

9. a) F; b) F; c) F; d) F

NOTES:

Exercise Ten
The Dynamic Ocean Floor

MATERIALS REQUIRED

The following materials are necessary to complete this exercise and should be available in the laboratory. The quantities depend upon the number of students in the laboratory and whether or not students are to work independently or in groups.

atlas, globe, or world wall map

TEXTBOOK REFERENCES

Tarbuck and Lutgens, *Earth Science*, 10th edition, 2002. Chapters 7 and 12

Tarbuck and Lutgens, *Earth Science*, 9th edition, 1999. Chapters 7 and 12

Lutgens and Tarbuck, *Foundations of Earth Science*, 3rd edition, 2002. Chapters 5 and 9

Murphy and Nance, *Earth Science Today*, 2001. Chapters 4 and 5

Skinner and Porter, *The Blue Planet*, 2nd edition, 1999. Chapter 8

Thompson and Turk, *Earth Science and the Environment*, 2nd edition, 1999. Chapters 5, 8 and 13

PROCEDURES AND STRATEGIES

- To conserve laboratory session time, questions 1 through 10, which review ocean floor features, could be assigned as pre-lab activities.

- Since an atlas, globe, or world map are the only additional materials required to complete the exercise, the entire exercise could be assigned as homework for completion outside the normal laboratory period.

- Some students may have difficulty visualizing sea-floor spreading and relating it to the paleomagnetism of the ocean floor. Therefore, we recommend that these concepts be presented and/or thoroughly reviewed prior to beginning the exercise.

- Students are required to do several calculations throughout the exercise. Although the calculations are presented in a straight forward, step-by-step, fashion, some students may require assistance.

ANSWERS TO EXERCISE TEN QUESTIONS

1. Mid-ocean ridge: a continuous mountainous ridge on the floor of all major ocean basins that varies in width from 500 to 5000 kilometers

   Mid-ocean ridge rift valley: a deep, linear valley extending along the axis of a mid-ocean ridge which forms as broken slabs are displaced downward along spreading centers on the ridge. The features are similar to continental rift valleys, such as those located in East Africa.

   Deep-ocean trench: a narrow, elongated depression on the floor of the ocean

2. see completed Figure 10.2

3. see completed Figure 10.2

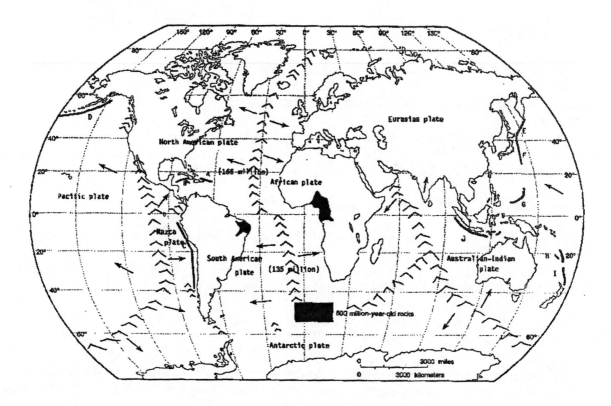

Figure 10.2

4. west

5. east

6. would

7. The ages of the ancient rocks would match, which supports the idea that the continents were once joined together.

8. see completed Figure 10.1

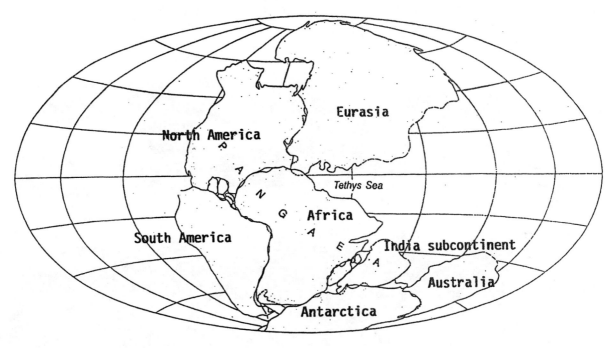

Figure 10.1

9. deep-ocean trenches

10. mid-ocean ridges

11. see completed Figure 10.2

12. 5

13. approximately 700,000 years ago

14. South

15. 2

16. less

17. yes (The earlier intervals of normal polarity represented on the figure are all shorter than the current period of normal polarity, which suggests that the current period may end at any time.)

18. see completed Figure 10.4

19. see completed Figure 10.4

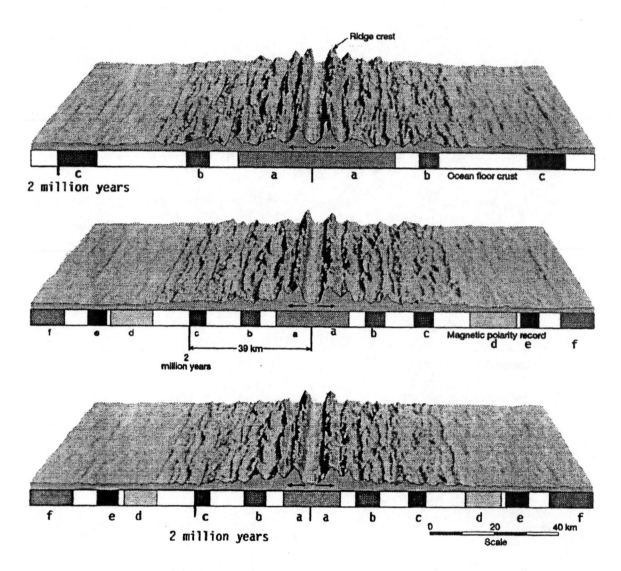

Figure 10.4

20. Pacific

21. a) approximately 80 kilometers; b) approximately 37 kilometers

22. Pacific Ocean basin: approximately 160 kilometers
    South Atlantic Ocean basin: approximately 78 kilometers
    North Atlantic Ocean basin: approximately 74 kilometers

23. b) Pacific: distance = 16,000,000 centimeters; rate of spreading = 8 cm/yr
    c) North Atlantic: distance = 7,400,000 cm; rate of spreading = 3.7 cm/yr

24. Minimum age: 3.8 million years; Maximum age: 5.6 million years

25. 500 kilometers; 50,000,000 centimeters (500 km x 1,000 m/km x 100 cm/m)

26. Maximum velocity: approximately 13.2 cm/yr (50 million cm divided by 3.8 miilion years)
    Minimum velocity: approximately 8.9 cm/yr (50 million cm divided by 5.6 million years)

27. Distance = 5800 kilometers = 580,000,000 centimeters (great circle method)(Answers will vary with the accuracy of measurements.)

28. Age of North Atlantic Basin: approximately 157,000,000 years (580,000,000 cm divided by 3.7 cm/yr) (Answers will vary with the accuracy of measurements.)

29. (distance = approximately 5200 km = 520,000,000 cm using Table 21.1, "Longitude as distance")

    Age of the South Atlantic basin: approximately 133,000,000 years (520,000,000 cm divided by 3.9 cm/yr) (Answers will vary with the accuracy of measurements.)

30. see completed Figure 10.2

31. divergent; a) spreading; b) mid-ocean ridges; c) construction

32. convergent;

    a) colliding;

    b) Oceanic-continental convergence: the leading edge of a plate capped with continental crust converges with oceanic crust, the less dense continental material apparently remains "floating," while the more dense oceanic slab sinks into the asthenosphere. This type of convergence produces deep-ocean trenches and often volcanoes on the land as magma from the partial melting of the descending slab rises. Feature: Cascade Range (or Sierra Nevada system, or the Andes)

    Oceanic-oceanic convergence: when two oceanic slabs converge, one descending beneath the other. This type of convergence causes volcanoes to form on the ocean floor from magma produced from the partial melting of a descending slab. Feature: Aleutian (Mariana, Tonga) islands

    Continental-continental convergence: when two plates carrying continental crust converge. Neither plate will subduct and the result is a collision between the two continental blocks that can form complex mountains; Feature: Himalayas (Alps, Appalachians, Urals)

33. transform; a) remains unchanged; b) transform faults; faults that roughly parallel the direction of plate movement and join offset segments of the ridge system

34. see completed Figure 10.7

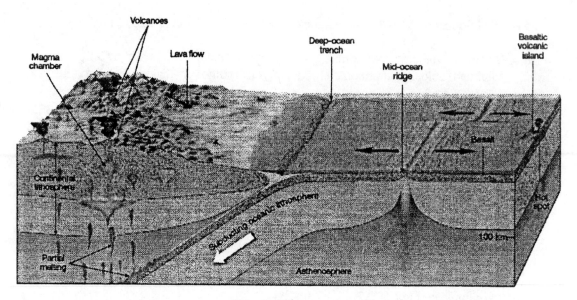

Figure 10.7

35. basalt

36. mid-ocean ridges and basaltic volcanic islands

37. hot spots; basalt

38. trenches

39. partially melt; volcanoes

ANSWERS TO EXERCISE TEN SUMMARY/REPORT PAGE QUESTIONS

1. see the following sketch

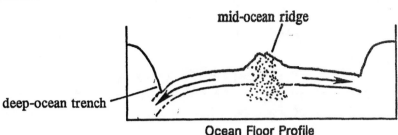

Ocean Floor Profile

2. deep-ocean trenches

3. primarily mid-ocean ridges

4. the plates that comprise Earth's lithosphere

5. Time intervals are recorded by the magnetic polarity reversals preserved in the oceanic crust across a section of the mid-ocean ridge. The distance that the ocean basin has opened along the ridge during a particular time interval recorded by the magnetic polarity reversals preserved in the oceanic crust can be measured. Knowing both the distance and time, the rate can be calculated by dividing the distance by the time.

6. Pacific Ocean basin: 8 cm/yr
    North Atlantic Ocean basin: 3.7 cm/yr

7. North Atlantic: 157 million years old (Answers will vary with the accuracy of measurements.)
    South Atlantic: 133 million years old (Answers will vary with the accuracy of measurements.)

8. approximately 13.2 cm/yr

9. see the following sketch

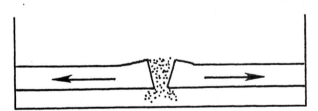

Profile of a Divergent Plate Boundary

Explanation: Along divergent plate boundaries, at the crests of oceanic ridges, material from the mantle will rise and create new sea floor between the plates.

10. Ocean floor volcanoes: form over hot spots in the asthenosphere from basaltic magma that rises to the ocean floor

    Volcanoes along continental margins bordering ocean trenches: form from lava that erupts from a pocket of magma in the continent. Partial melting of an oceanic plate as it descends beneath the continent is the source of the magma.

11. Plate tectonics is a far more encompassing theory than continental drift. According to the plate tectonics model, the upprermost mantle, along with the overlying crust, behaves as a strong, rigid layer, known as the lithosphere. This outermost shell overlies a weaker region in the mantle known as the asthenosphere. Further, the lithosphere is broken into numerous segnents called plates, which are in motion and are continually changing in shape and size.

The lines of evidence that support plate tectonics include: 1) paleomagnetism (polar wandering and magnetic reversals), 2) earthquake patterns, 3) the age and distribution of ocean sediments, and 4) evidence from ocean floor volcanoes that are, or were, located over hot spots.

NOTES:

Exercise Eleven
Waves, Currents, and Tides

MATERIALS REQUIRED

The following materials are necessary to complete this exercise and should be available in the laboratory. The quantities depend upon the number of students in the laboratory and whether or not students are to work independently or in groups.

atlas or world wall map

> **NOTE**: When working with topographic maps, using a hand lens or sheet magnifier often helps reduce student frustration.

TEXTBOOK REFERENCES

Tarbuck and Lutgens, *Earth Science*, 10th edition, 2002. Chapter 14

Tarbuck and Lutgens, *Earth Science*, 9th edition, 1999. Chapter 13

Lutgens and Tarbuck, *Foundations of Earth Science*, 3rd edition, 2002. Chapter 10

Murphy and Nance, *Earth Science Today*, 2001. Chapter 9

Skinner and Porter, *The Blue Planet*, 2nd edition, 1999. Chapter 11

Thompson and Turk, *Earth Science and the Environment*, 2nd edition, 1999. Chapter 14

PROCEDURES AND STRATEGIES

- Most students should be able to complete this exercise within the time alloted for a normal laboratory session. However, should you decide to conserve laboratory time, any of the four sections (waves, currents, shoreline features, or tides) can be completed as homework, outside the laboratory.

- Since an atlas or world map are the only materials that are required to complete the exercise, the entire exercise could be assigned as homework and completed outside the laboratory.

- Students are required to do some calculations; however, they are introduced in a step-by-step fashion and should not present any great difficulty.

- If you have access to aerial photographs, stereograms, and/or topographic maps that illustrate various coastal landforms and features, we recommend that they be placed in the laboratory for the students to observe.

ANSWERS TO EXERCISE ELEVEN QUESTIONS

1. wave crest: C; wave trough: E; wave height: D; wavelength: B; depth of negligible water particle motion: A

2. Below 12 meters (which is 0.5 of the wavelength)

3. Factor 1: wind speed
   Factor 2: length of time the wind has blown
   Factor 3: fetch, the distance that the wind has traveled across the open water

4. circular; elliptical

5. ahead of

6. increase; shorter

7. falling forward

8. 6.3 m/sec

9. Wavelength = 16 meters (2.0 m/sec x 8.0 sec)
   a) Wave base = 8 meters (0.5 of the wavelength)
   b) 1

10. wavelength and depth of water

11. No. The fact that the wavelength is 80 meters and the waves are beginning to break indicates that the depth of water is approximately 4 meters (0.05 x 80 meters) and too deep for a person to stand safely on the bottom.

12. In contrast to a surf zone, the rising and falling waves indicate that deep water is present along the shoreline.

13. By reducing the depth of water off-shore, breakwaters will cause waves to break and loose energy, thereby protecting boats near the shore from the force of large breaking waves by creating a quiet-water zone.

14. Velocity = 375 miles per hour (V = L/T, V = 125 miles/0.33 hours)

15. 40 feet (0.5L)

16. 4 (0.05L)

17. - 19. see completed Figure 11.3

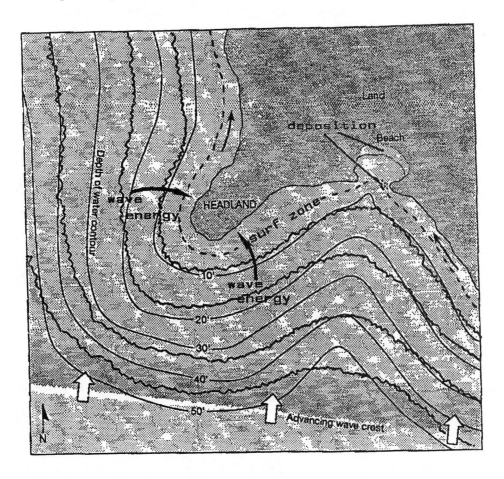

Figure 11.3

20. headland

21. Over a long period, the concentrated energy from wave impact will erode the headland and straighten an irregular coastline.

22. see completed Figure 21.8, Exercise Twenty-one, (Students who have completed Exercise Nine and HAVE NOT done Exercise Twenty-one should see ALTERNATE completed Figure 21.8, Exercise Twenty-one)

23. West Wind Drift

24. Gulf Stream; warm

25. California; cold

26. clockwise; counterclockwise

27. ABW (Antarctic Bottom Water): cold and highly saline (the densest water in all the oceans) that forms in the Antarctic, sinks, and flows northward along the ocean floor as far as 20°N latitude

NADW (North Atlantic Deep Water): cold and saline water thought to form when warm and highly saline Gulf Stream waters reach the Arctic region near Greenland. This dense water sinks to the bottom of the North Atlantic Basin, overrides the ABW water, and flows almost as far south as the Antarctic region.

AIW (Antarctic Intermediate Water): forms when the very salty water of the Brazil Current is chilled, sinks, and flows northward

MW (Mediterranean Water): forms when the highly saline water of the Mediterranean Sea is chilled, sinks, and flows westward into the Atlantic

28. The very high density is the result of the facts that the water is cold and highly saline because salts that are excluded from sea ice that forms in the Antarctic are added to the surface water.

29. see completed Figure 11.3

30. The longshore current is interrupted or weakens and sediment may be deposited.

31. see completed Figure 11.3

32. Wave refraction in the bay causes waves to diverge and expend less energy. The result is weakened wave activity and the accumulation of sediments.

33. see completed Figure 11.5

34. groin: a barrier built at a right angle to a beach for the purpose of trapping sand that is moving parallel to the shore

pair of jetties: barriers that extend into the ocean at the entrance to a river or harbor that confine the flow of water and prevent deposition in the channel

35. see completed Figure 11.5A

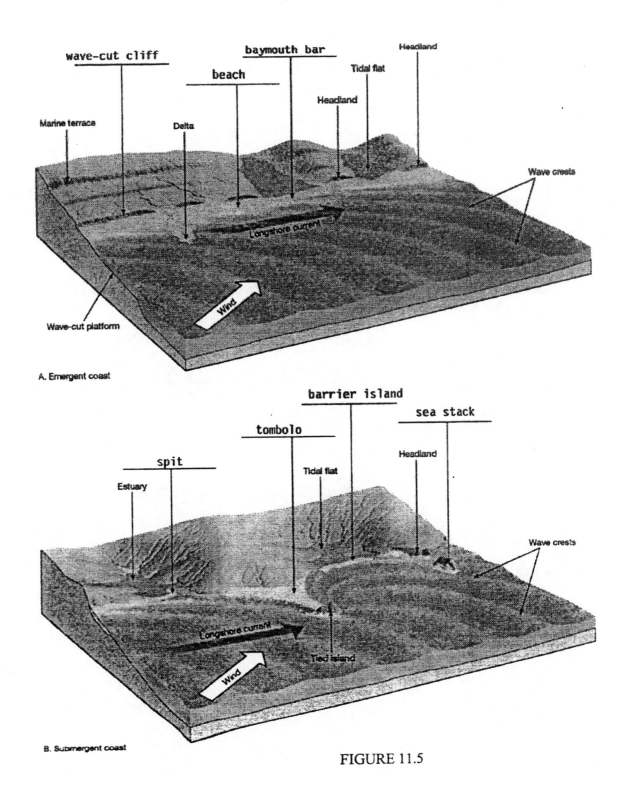

wave-cut cliff

baymouth bar

Headland

beach

Tidal flat

Marine terrace

Delta

Headland

Headland

Wave crests

Longshore current

Wind

Wave-cut platform

A. Emergent coast

barrier island

sea stack

tombolo

Tidal flat

Headland

spit

Estuary

Wave crests

Longshore current

Tied island

Wind

B. Submergent coast

FIGURE 11.5

36. submergent

37. estuaries

38. sea stacks; wave erosion on opposite sides of a headland forms a sea arch which collapses, leav-ing an isolated remnant of the headland

39. spit

40 (east to west).

41. Sand will accumulate on the east side of the groin. The west side will be "sand starved" and eroded.

42. The lake is an estuary that has been closed-off by the formation of a baymouth bar at its mouth.

43. Diurnal tides: a single high and low water height each tidal day

    Semidiurnal tides: two high and two low tides each tidal day, with a relatively small difference in the high and low water heights

    Mixed tides: usually two high and two low waters each day with a large inequality in high water heights, low water heights, or both

44. Diurnal tides occur at: Pakhoi
    Semidiurnal tides: New York
    Mixed tides: Port Adelaide, Seattle, Los Angeles, Honolulu

45. Seattle

46. Mixed tides are prevalent along the Pacific coast, while semidiurnal tides are more common along the Atlantic coast.

47. changes

48. The tidal ranges at New York are greatest during the times of new and full moon.

49. see the following diagrams and explanations

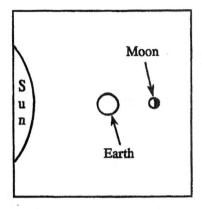

Spring tides: Spring tides, which create the largest daily tidal range, occur near the times of new and full moon when the sun and moon are aligned and their gravitational forces are added together.

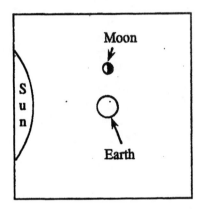

Neap tides: Neap tides, which create less of a daily tidal range, occur about the times of the first and third quarters of the moon when the gravitational forces of the sun and moon on Earth are at right angles, and each partially offsets the influence of the other.

50. (On Figure 11.8: at New York, spring tides occur during the periods of September 6-10 and 21-26; neap tides occur September 1-4, 14-18, and 29-.)

51. No. Other factors that influence tides are the shape of the coastline and the configuration of the ocean basin.

52. Criterion 1: a tidal range greater than 8 meters (25 feet)
    Criterion 2: a narrow, enclosed bay

For Web-based laboratory experiences related to this exercise, make sure you have your students investigate our Website at:

http://www.prenhall.com/earthsciencelab

NOTES:

ANSWERS TO EXERCISE ELEVEN SUMMARY/REPORT PAGE QUESTIONS

1. see completed Figure 11.9

    As waves move from deep water into shallow water, particle motion changes from circular to elliptical, wavelength decreases, and wave height increases. In very shallow water, where the depth is about 0.05 of the wavelength, the crest of the wave begins to fall forward and the wave breaks.

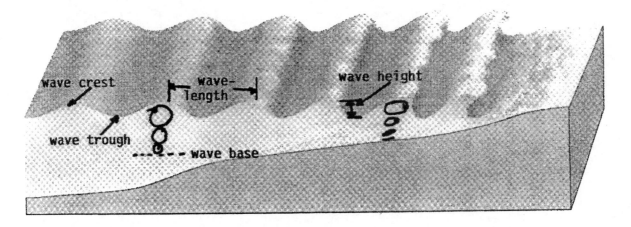

Figure 11.9

2. The waves will be refracted (bent) and reach the shore approximately parallel to the shoreline.

3. Spit: elongated ridge of sand, often with a curved end, that projects from the land into the mouth of an adjacent bay, formed by beach drift and longshore currents

    Stack: (or sea stack), an isolated erosional remnant along a coast produced when wave erosion on opposite sides of a headland forms a sea arch which collapses

    Tombolo: ridge of sand that connects an island to the mainland, forms in much the same manner as a spit

    Estuary: funnel-shaped inlet of the sea that forms when a rise in sea level or subsidence of land caused the mouth of a river to be flooded

4. Point Reyes: headland
    Drakes Estero: estuary
    Chimney Rock: sea stack

5. counterclockwise

6. East coast: Gulf Stream; warm
    West coast: California; cold

NOTES:

Exercise Twelve
Earth-Sun Relations

MATERIALS REQUIRED

The following materials are necessary to complete this exercise and should be available in the laboratory. The quantities depend upon the number of students in the laboratory and whether or not students are to work independently or in groups.

    globe
    large rubber band or string

TEXTBOOK REFERENCES

Tarbuck and Lutgens, *Earth Science*, 10th edition, 2002. Chapter 15

Tarbuck and Lutgens, *Earth Science*, 9th edition, 1999. Chapter 14

Lutgens and Tarbuck, *Foundations of Earth Science*, 3rd edition, 2002. Chapter 11

Murphy and Nance, *Earth Science Today*, 2001. Chapters 11 and 12

Skinner and Porter, *The Blue Planet*, 2nd edition, 1999. Chapter 12

Thompson and Turk, *Earth Science and the Environment*, 2nd edition, 1999. Chapter 415

PROCEDURES AND STRATEGIES

- Most students should be able to complete the entire exercise within the time allotted for a normal laboratory session.

- Since a globe and large rubber band or string are the only additional materials necessary to complete the exercise, by eliminating question 18 (or having the students use Table 12.1 instead of a rubber band or string) the exercise could be assigned as homework and done outside the labor-atory session.

- To achieve maximum benefit from the exercise, we recommend (although it is not necessary) that students should have already done the noon sun angle measurements in Exercise 17, Astronomical Observations.

- Prior to beginning the exercise, a review of the relation between the latitude of the overhead noon sun and the angle of the noon sun at various latitudes may be helpful.

- Question 42 presents a good opportunity for class discussion on the applications of knowing the noon sun angle (navigation, architectural design, etc.).

ANSWERS TO EXERCISE TWELVE QUESTIONS

1. see completed Figure 12.1

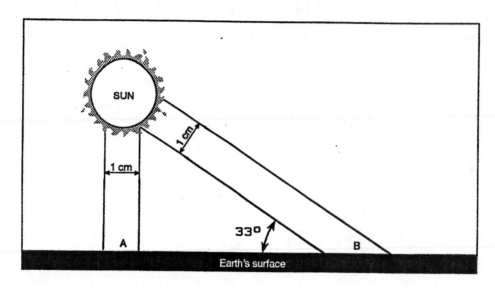

Figure 12.1

2. 33° (approximate)

3. Point A: 10 mm (1 cm); point B: 17 mm

4. B

5. A

6. 8 centimeters (80 millimeters)

7. Each centimeter would equal _10_ % and each millimeter would equal _1.25_ %

8. 0° - 30° = 40 mm = 50%
    30° - 60° = 29 mm = 36%
    60° - 90° = 11 mm = 14%

9. Angle a: 90°; angle c: 30°; angle d: 0°

10. As the angle of the Sun's rays increases, each 30° segment of Earth receives more radiation.

11. The fact that Earth is nearly spherical causes solar radiation to be concentrated at latitudes where the solar beam is overhead (90° above the horizon) and progressively less concentrated where the solar beam strikes the surface at angles less than 90°.

12. Tropic of Cancer: Mexico, Western Sahara, Mauritania, Mali, Algeria, Libya, Egypt, Saudi Arabia, United Arab Emirates, Oman, India, Bangladesh, Assam, Burma, China, Taiwan

Tropic of Capricorn: Chile, Argentina, Paraguay, Brazil, Namibia, Botswana, South Africa, Mozambique, Madagascar, Australia

Arctic Circle: United States, Canada, Greenland, Norway, Sweden, Finland, Russia

13. see completed Figure 12.3

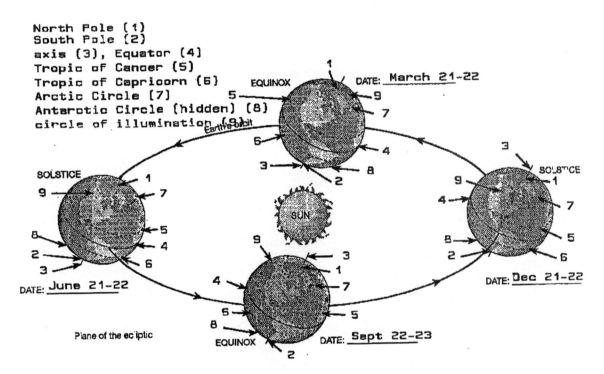

North Pole (1)
South Pole (2)
axis (3), Equator (4)
Tropic of Cancer (5)
Tropic of Capricorn (6)
Arctic Circle (7)
Antarctic Circle (hidden) (8)
circle of illumination (9)

Figure 12.3

14. Northern Hemisphere: summer solstice
    Southern Hemisphere: winter solstice

15. Tropic of Cancer

16. 23 °N (Tropic of Cancer)

17. 40°N: south
    10°N: north

18. 70°N: 24 hrs; 40°S: approximately 9 hrs; 40°N: approximately 15 hrs; 90°S: 0 hrs; 0°: 12 hrs

19. 24 hrs of daylight; 24 hrs of darkness

20. Northern Hemisphere: winter solstice
    Southern Hemisphere: summer solstice

21. Tropic of Capricorn

22. Southern

23. south

24. 90°N: 0 hrs; 40°S: approximately 15; 40°N: approximately 9 hrs; 90°S: 24 hrs (for a period of 6 months); 0°: 12 hrs

25. March 21: vernal, or spring, equinox
    September 22: autumnal equinox

26. March 21: autumnal equinox
    September 22: vernal, or spring, equinox

27. equator

28. 0° (equator)

29. north

30. The circle of illumination passes through both poles on these dates.

31. Everywhere on Earth will have 12 hours of daylight on March 21 and September 22.

32. [On Figure 12.4, the analemma, students are to draw and label the: equator (0° latitude); Tropic of Cancer (23 °N latitude); and Tropic of Capricorn (23 °S latitude)]

33. December 10: 22 °S; March 21: 0°; May 5: 16°N; June 22: 23 °N; August 10: 15 °N; October 15: 8°S

34. 23 °N, Tropic of Cancer and 23 °S, Tropic of Capricorn

35. September 22-23 and March 21-22; equinoxes

36. Throughout the year the overhead noon Sun migrates between the Tropic of Cancer (23 °N) on June 21-22, the Tropic of Capricorn (23 °S) on December 21-22, and back to the Tropic of Cancer. The intensity and duration of solar radiation is greatest in the Northern Hemisphere on June 21-22 and in the Southern Hemisphere on December 21-22.

37. Table 12.2 completed

	Mar 21	Apr 11	Jun 21	Dec 22
Latitude of over-head noon sun	(0°)	(8°N)	(23 °N)	(23 °S)
		Noon Sun Angle		
90°N	0°	8°	23 °	0° (or -23 °)
40°N	(50°)	58°	73 °	(26 °)
0°	90°	82°	(66 °)	66 °
20°S	70°	(62°)	46 °	86 °

38. 0° (equator)

39. answers will vary with the date and latitude

40. Date of maximum noon sun angle: June 21-22; Date of minimum noon Sun angle: December 21-22 (assuming a Northern Hemisphere location); answers for angle will vary with latitude

41. answers will vary with latitude

42. architectural design, setting solar panels, navigation

NOTE: Question 42 presents a good opportunity for class discussion on the applications of knowing the noon Sun angle.

43. 72°S (approximate)

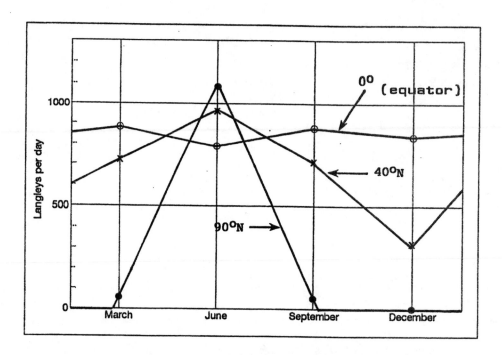

44. 43°N (approximate)

Figure 12.5

45. see completed Figure 12.5 The overhead noon Sun passes over the equator twice a year at the times of the equinoxes. The result is maximum intensity of solar radiation on these dates.

46. In June, both 40°N and the North Pole are receiving their maximum intensities and longest durations. Although the noon sun angle is lower at the North Pole than at the equator, the fact that the pole is receiving 24 hours of daylight causes it to receive a greater total quantity of solar radiation.

47. In December, due to the inclination of Earth's axis, the North Pole is experiencing 24 hours of darkness.

48. At 40°S - March: 700; June: 325; September: 700; December: 950

   Explanation: Table 12.3 illustrates the seasonal distribution of solar radiation at 40° latitude in the Northern Hemisphere. The seasons are reversed in the Southern Hemisphere; June, the Northern Hemisphere summer, corresponds to December in the Southern Hemisphere and December, the Northern Hemisphere winter, corresponds to June in the Southern Hemisphere.

For Web-based laboratory experiences related to this exercise, make sure you have your students investigate our Website at:

http://www.prenhall.com/earthsciencelab

ANSWERS TO EXERCISE TWELVE SUMMARY/REPORT PAGE QUESTIONS

1. $0° - 30° = 50\,mm = 50\%$
   $30° - 60° = 36\,mm = 36\%$
   $60° - 90° = 14\,mm = 14\%$

2. March 22: 40°N (12 hrs); 0° (12 hrs); 90°S (12 hrs)
   December 22: 40°N (9 hrs, approximate); 0° (12 hrs); 90°S (24 hrs)

3. 40°N: 58° noon Sun angle; 0°: 82° noon Sun angle

4. As the noon Sun angle increase, a greater quantity of solar radiation will be received by each square centimeter.

5. see completed Figure 12.6

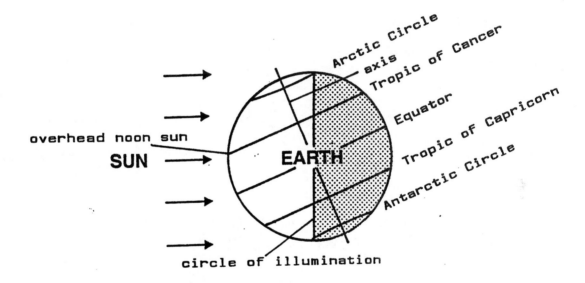

Figure 12.6

6. Intensity and duration vary because, as Earth revolves around the Sun, its axis, which is inclined 23 ° from being perpendicular to the plane of the ecliptic (or 66 ° from the plane of the ecliptic), remains oriented to the same place in the sky which causes the latitude of the over-head noon Sun to migrate between the Tropics of Cancer (23 °N) and Capricorn (23 °S).

7. Date of maximum noon sun angle: June 21-22; Date of minimum noon Sun angle: December 21-22 (assuming a Northern Hemisphere location); answers for angle will vary with latitude

8. answers will vary with latitude

9. Intensity and duration are greatest on the date of the summer solstice and least on the date of the winter solstice.

10. Latitude: 55°N

NOTES:

Exercise Thirteen
Atmospheric Heating

MATERIALS REQUIRED

The following materials are necessary to complete this exercise and should be available in the laboratory. The quantities depend upon the number of students in the laboratory and whether or not students are to work independently or in groups.

light source
black and silver containers
two thermometers

wood splint
beaker of sand
beaker of water

NOTE: The quantity of each of the items depends on whether or not the students are to conduct the experiments individually, in groups, or the experiments will be presented as demonstrations.

TEXTBOOK REFERENCES

Tarbuck and Lutgens, *Earth Science*, 10th edition, 2002. Chapters 15

Tarbuck and Lutgens, *Earth Science*, 8th edition, 1999. Chapters 14

Lutgens and Tarbuck, *Foundations of Earth Science*, 3nd edition, 2002. Chapter 11

Murphy and Nance, *Earth Science Today*, 2001. Chapter 11 and 12

Skinner and Porter, *The Blue Planet*, 2nd edition, 1999. Chapters 12 and 14

Thompson and Turk, *Earth Science and the Environment*, 2nd edition, 1999. Chapters 15 and 17

PROCEDURES AND STRATEGIES

- Due to the fact that two in-lab experiments (albedo and land/water heating) are included in this exercise, to conserve laboratory time, we recommend that questions 1 through 18 be assigned as pre-lab activities. Also, questions 26 through 64, which require no additional materials, could be assigned as homework to be completed either before or after the scheduled laboratory session.

- Prior to beginning the exercise, a review of albedo and the mechanism for heating Earth's atmosphere may be appropriate.

- To conduct the experiments, we recommend that students work in groups of 2 - 4.

- For those with limited access to materials, we recommend that, at least, the experiments be done as demonstrations and that the data be used by the students to complete the appropriate questions.

- The specific data for the experiments collected by each student group will vary. This may present a good opportunity to discuss the controls and variables of the experiments.

ANSWERS TO EXERCISE THIRTEEN QUESTIONS

1. Intensity of solar radiation: the angle that a solar beam strikes a surface
    Duration of solar radiation: the length of daylight

2. Table 13.1 completed

	March 21		June 21	
	Noon Sun Angle	**Length of Day**	**Noon Sun Angle**	**Length of Day**
40°N	50°	12 hrs	73 °	15 hrs (approx.)
0°	90°	12 hrs	66 °	12 hrs
40°S	50°	12 hrs	26 °	9 hrs (approx.)

3. As Earth revolves around the Sun, its axis, which is inclined 23 ° from being perpendicular to the plane of the ecliptic (or 66 ° from the plane of the ecliptic), remains oriented toward the same place in the sky which causes the latitude of the overhead noon Sun to migrate between the Tropics of Cancer (23 °N) and Capricorn (23 °S). The result is that the intensity and duration of solar radiation varies throughout the year at any particular latitude.

4. 30%

5. 20%

6. 50%

7. Two and a half

8. visible

9. infrared

10. Infrared

11. Carbon dioxide; water vapor

12. lesser

13. less; more

14. greater

15. more; less

16. Other factors remaining the same, as the angle (intensity) increases a square meter would receive more solar radiation.

17. Other factors remaining the same, as the length of daylight increases a square meter would receive more solar radiation.

18. Solar radiation, primarily in the form of visible radiation, is absorbed at Earth's surface. When Earth releases this radiation it is in the form of infrared radiation which is absorbed by the gases of the atmosphere and heats the atmosphere from the ground up.

19. (The specific data collected from the albedo experiment and recorded in Table 13.2 and on Figure 13.3 will vary.) The black container heats up faster and gets hotter than the silver container.

20. High albedos: snow, sand
    Low albedos: dark soil, blacktop road, green forest

21. colder; Explanation: Snow, with a high albedo, will absorb less solar radiation and hence have less to return back to the atmosphere as infrared radiation. A dark-colored, barren field has a low albedo and will absorb more solar radiation and return more terrestrial (infrared) radiation back to the atmosphere. The result is more atmospheric heating over the dark-colored, barren field.

22. Light-colored clothes have a higher albedo and therefore less radiation will be absorbed.

23. dark- (more absorption by the dark surface will aid in heating)

24. (The specific data collected from the land and water heating experiment and recorded in Table 13.3 and on Figure 13.5 will vary.)

    a) dry sand heats up faster and gets hotter than water

    b) dry sand heats up faster and gets hotter than wet sand

25. Reason 1: The specific heat is far greater for water than for land.
    Reason 2: Land surfaces are opaque, so heat is absorbed only at the surface.
    Reason 3: The water that is heated often mixes with other water, thus distributing the heat.
    Reason 4: Evaporation (a cooling process) from water bodies is greater than that from land.

26. B

27. B

28. B

29. B

30. A

31. along a coast

32. mid-continent

33. Mid-continent locations often experience a greater annual temperature range and reach their maximum temperatures earlier than coastal locations.

34. 6 AM

35. 4 to 5 PM

36. 22°F (13°C)

37. 69°F (21°C)

38. It takes time for Earth's surface to absorb solar radiation, heat up, and return terrestrial radiation to the atmosphere for heating.

39. Throughout the night Earth's surface has been releasing terrestrial radiation.

40. Cloud cover during the day often lowers the daily maximum by preventing solar radiation from reaching the surface. At night, cloud cover often causes warmer surface temperatures by preventing the escape of heat from the lower atmosphere.

41. see completed Figure 13.7

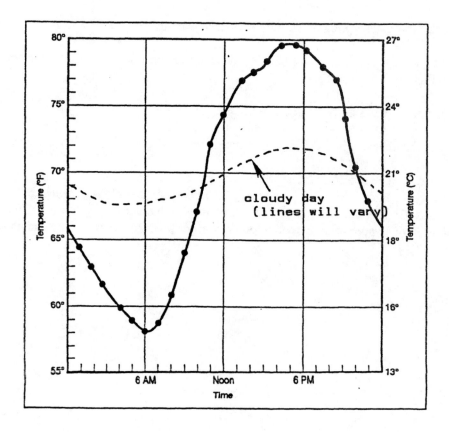

Figure 13.7

42. east-west

43. In general, temperature decreases from the equator to the poles because the intensity of solar radiation decreases.

44. Warmest global temperature: 35°C in July over the southwestern United States, Algeria, Libya, Niger, Chad, Sudan, Saudi Arabia, and Iran

   Coldest global temperature: -40°C in January over east central Russia

45. land

46. Coastal Norway at 60°N: 14°C (25°F)
   Siberia at 60°N, 120°E: 45°C (81°F)
   On the equator over the center of the Atlantic Ocean: approximately 1°C (approximately 2°F)

47. The large annual range in temperature is due to the effect of being located in the interior of a large expanse of land.

48. The influence of the ocean causing a more uniform temperature throughout the year.

49. The intensity and duration of solar radiation change little throughout the year and the influence of ocean water.

50. answers will vary with location

51. In January, the 5°C isotherm deflects southward because, at that same latitude, the land is cooler than the water.

52. In July, the 20°C isotherm deflects northward because, at that same latitude, the land is warmer than the water.

53. Because the Southern Hemisphere is essentially water and the temperature extremes caused by the heating and cooling of land are of minor consequence.

54. Temperatures on Earth follow the movement of the overhead noon Sun.

55. see completed Figure 13.9

56. see completed Figure 13.9

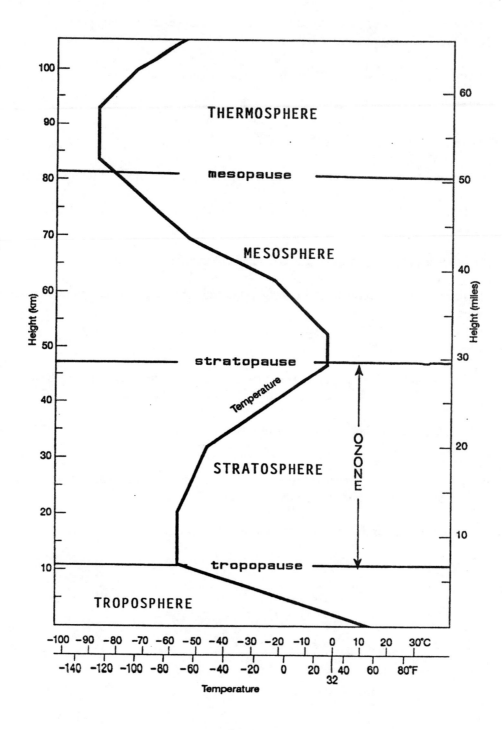

Figure 13.9

57. 10 km: -58°C (-72°F); 50 km: -2°C (30°F); 80 km: -79°C (-110°F)

58. Temperature decrease with altitude in the troposphere: the source of the heat in the troposphere is Earth's surface, therefore most of the heating occurs at the bottom of the troposphere

   Temperature increase in the stratosphere: the atmosphere's ozone absorbs ultraviolet radiation from the Sun which causes heating

   Temperature increase in the thermosphere: temperatures increase due to the absorption of very short wave solar radiation by atoms of oxygen and nitrogen

59. Ozone in the stratosphere absorbs ultraviolet radiation from the Sun. A decrease of ozone in the stratosphere will result in more ultraviolet radiation from the Sun reaching Earth's surface.

60. -10°F (-23°C)

61. 50°F: approximately 8,600 feet; (10°C: approximately 2,600 meters)
    0°C: approximately 4,200 meters; (32°F: approximately 13,700 feet)

62. A surface temperature inversion develops close to the ground on clear and relatively calm nights. It forms because the ground is a more effective radiator than the air above. This being the case, radiation from the ground to the clear night sky causes more rapid cooling at the surface than higher in the atmosphere.

63. Temperature inversions can cause atmospheric pollutants to become trapped in a relatively narrow zone near the ground because the mixing depth of the atmosphere is significantly restricted.

64. 30°F and 10 mph: 16°F windchill equivalent temperature
    -5°F and 20 mph: -46°F windchill equivalent temperature
    -20°F and 30 mph: -79°F windchill equivalent temperature

For Web-based laboratory experiences related to this exercise, make sure you have your students investigate our Website at:

http://www.prenhall.com/earthsciencelab

ANSWERS TO EXERCISE THIRTEEN SUMMARY/REPORT PAGE QUESTIONS

1. Atmospheric absorption: 20%
   Absorption by Earth's surface: 50%

2. Less ozone in the atmosphere: less ultraviolet radiation from the Sun will be absorbed and more will reach Earth's surface

   More carbon dioxide in the atmosphere: more terrestrial (infrared) radiation will be absorbed by the atmosphere and it will become warmer

   A surface with a high albedo: less terrestrial (infrared) radiation will be returned to the atmosphere and consequently less heating of the atmosphere

3. Earth's atmosphere is heated from below by absorbing terrestrial (infrared) radiation that is released at Earth's surface.

4. answers will vary

5. Dark colors are more efficient absorbers of radiation and therefore heat up faster and get hotter than light colored surfaces.

6. answers will vary

7. Given equal amounts of radiation, land will heat up faster and get hotter than water.

8. Highest average monthly temperatures: occur in July over land in the southwestern United States, north central Africa, and the Middle East

   Lowest average monthly temperatures: occur in January over land in east central Russia

9. Temperatures in the Northern Hemisphere are influenced by land; while temperatures in the Southern Hemisphere are controlled by water.

10. Environmental lapse rate: the rate of temperature decrease with increasing altitude in the troposphere

    Windchill equivalent temperature: an expression that relates wind speed to the temperature we perceive

    Troposphere: the lowermost layer of the atmosphere, generally characterized by a decrease of temperature with increasing altitude

Exercise Fourteen
Atmospheric Moisture, Pressure, and Wind

MATERIALS REQUIRED

The following materials are necessary to complete this exercise and should be available in the laboratory. The quantities depend upon the number of students in the laboratory and whether or not students are to work independently or in groups.

psychrometer or hygrometer
beaker, ice, thermometer
barometer
atlas

NOTE: Students will require some instruction on the operation and reading of a psychrometer (or hygrometer) and a barometer.

TEXTBOOK REFERENCES

Tarbuck and Lutgens, *Earth Science*, 10th edition, 2002. Chapters 16 and 17

Tarbuck and Lutgens, *Earth Science*, 9th edition, 1999. Chapters 15 and 16

Lutgens and Tarbuck, *Foundations of Earth Science*, 3nd edition, 2002. Chapters 12 and 13

Murphy and Nance, *Earth Science Today*, 2001. Chapters 11 and 12

Skinner and Porter, *The Blue Planet*, 2nd edition, 1999. Chapters 12 and 13

Thompson and Turk, *Earth Science and the Environment*, 2nd edition, 1999. Chapter 16

PROCEDURES AND STRATEGIES

- Due to the facts that this exercise covers atmospheric moisture, pressure, and wind as well as a simple experiment on dew-point temperature, it may require more than the normal time allotted for a single laboratory session to complete. The following are a few suggestions for conserving laboratory time:

    1. Divide the exercise into two parts; a) atmospheric moisture, and b) pressure and wind.

    2. Assign questions 1 through 19 as pre-lab activities.

    3. Assign the section on pressure and wind (with the exception of question 52, which requires reading a barometer if one is available in the lab) to be completed as homework outside the normal laboratory session.

    4. Eliminate question 24, which is a simple experiment on dew-point temperature.

- Depending on whether or not you have access to a psychrometer or hygrometer, some adjustments to question 23 may be necessary.

- For those with limited access to materials, the dew-point temperature experiment, question 24, could be done as a demonstration.

ANSWERS TO EXERCISE FOURTEEN QUESTIONS

1. see completed Figure 14.2

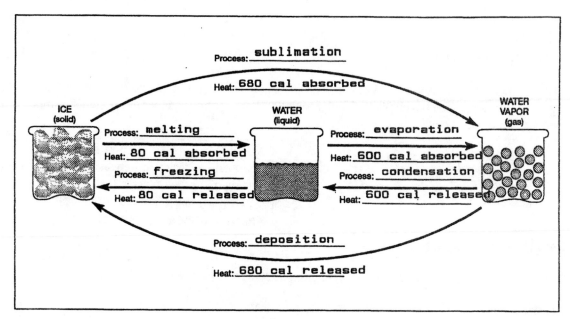

Figure 14.2

2. less

3. more

4. same as

5. see completed Figure 14.3

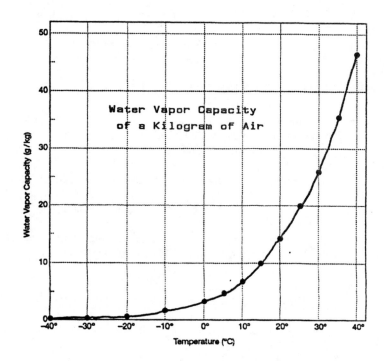

Figure 14.3

6. 40°C: 47 g/kg; 20°C: 14 g/kg; 0°C: 3.5 g/kg; -20°C: 0.75 g/kg

7. from 10°C to 15°C: increases; 3 grams
    from 35°C to 40°C: increases; 12 grams

8. As the air temperature increases the water vapor capacity also increases, but at an increasing rate. For example, as illustrated in question 7, raising the air temperature from 10°C to 15°C raises the water vapor capacity by 3 grams per kilogram of air while raising the air temperature from 35°C to 40°C raises the capacity by four times this amount.

9. 15°C: 2 g/kg (content) divided by 10 g/kg (capacity) = 0.20 = 20% relative humidity
    15°C: 5 g/kg divided by 10 g/kg = 0.50 = 50% relative humidity
    15°C: 7 g/kg divided by 10 g/kg = 0.70 = 70% relative humidity

10. raise; lower

11. 25°C: 5 g/kg (content) divided by 20 g/kg (capacity) = 0.25 = 25% relative humidity
    15°C: 5 g/kg divided by 10 g/kg = 0.50 = 50% relative humidity
     5°C: 5 g/kg divided by 5 g/kg = 1.00 = 100% relative humidity

12. raise; lower

13. Heating the air will lower the relative humidity. To lessen the effect, moisture can be added to the air with a humidifier.

14. The relative humidity of the air in the basement will increase as the temperature is lowered.

15. 1) relative humidity can be changed by adding or removing water vapor to or from the air
    2) relative humidity can be changed by raising or lowering the air temperature

16. Summer: capacity = 20 g/kg (at 25°C); content = 8 g/kg (0.40 of 20 g/kg)
    Winter: capacity = 5 g/kg (at 5°C); content = 4.5 g/kg (0.90 of 5 g/kg)

17. Relative humidity is a function of air temperature (and the water vapor capacity of the air at that temperature). As illustrated in question 16, simply to assume that air with a 40% relative humidity has less water vapor per kilogram of air than air with a 90% relative humidity can be misleading.

18. 10°C

19. Relative humidity = 50%; Dew-point temperature = 15°C

20. 20°C (dry-bulb) and 18°C (wet-bulb); difference = 2; relative humidity = 82%
    32°C (dry-bulb) and 25°C (wet-bulb); difference = 7; relative humidity = 56%

21. As the difference in the dry-bulb and wet-bulb temperatures increases, the relative humidity decreases.

22. 8°C (dry-bulb) and 6°C (wet-bulb): difference = 2; dew-point temperature = 3°C
    30°C (dry-bulb) and 24°C (wet-bulb): difference = 6; dew-point temperature = 21°C

23. answers will vary

24. a) answers will vary; b) temperature should agree fairly well with the dew-point temperature of the air in the room

25. 2 grams [7 g/kg (at 10°C) minus 5 g/kg (at 5°C)]

26. 5°C: 5 grams; -10°C: 8 grams

27. The dew-point temperature of the air has been reached, or exceeded, at that altitude and condensation has occurred.

28. 6 A.M.; 1

29. 6 A.M.; 1

30. 4 P.M., 1

31. At 6 A.M. on day 1 the air temperature is lowest (below the dew-point temperature) and relative humidity is at its maximum. At 4 P.M. on day 1 the air temperature is highest and the relative humidity is at its lowest. In general, as air temperature increases the relative humidity decreases and as air temperature decreases the relative humidity increases.

32. Yes, at approximately 5 to 6 A.M. on day 1 when the air temperature dropped below the dew-point temperature.

33. Capacity: 20 g/kg; Content: 10 g/kg; Dew-point temperature: 15°C

34. unsaturated

35. cool; dry; 1

36. 20°C (25°C - 5°C)

37. will not

38. 1,000 meters; condense

39. cool; 0.5°C

40. -5°C [15°C (at 1,000 meters) minus 20° (4,000 meters to summit x 0.5° per 100 meters) of additional cooling to the summit]

41. increase

42. unsaturated; dry; 1

43. decrease

44. 25°C [-5°C (at the summit) plus 30° (3,000 meters x 1° per 100 meters) of warming to the plateau]

45. Air will warm by compression as it descends on the leeward side of a mountain. As air warms, its relative humidity will decrease (assuming no additional water is added to the air by evaporation) and cause dry conditions on the leeward side.

46. For precipitation to form, millions of cloud droplets must coalesce (join together) into droplets large enough to sustain themselves during their descent.

47. Rain: In a cloud, ice crystals form into snowflakes which, when the surface temperature is above 4°C (39°F), usually melt before they reach the ground and continue their descent as rain.

    Snow: usually occurs when surface temperatures are cold (below 4°C) and snowflakes do not melt as they descend to the ground.

    Sleet: when a layer of air with temperatures above freezing overlies a subfreezing layer near the ground, raindrops leave the warmer air and solidify as they fall through the colder air below, reaching the ground as small pellets of ice.

48. equatorial and tropical regions

49. low

50. answers will vary

51. Average annual precipitation is highest along the coast in the Pacific northwest (160 cm), least west of the 100°W meridian (-40 to 80 cm), and moderate east of the 100°W meridian (80 to 160 cm).

52. answers will vary

53. decreases; less

54. most

55. millibars

56. add

57.   see completed Figure 14.10

58.   see completed Figure 14.10

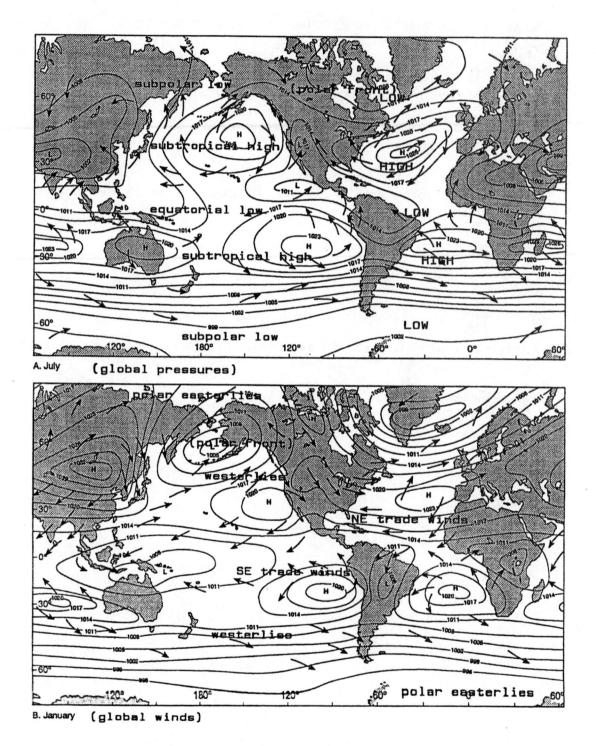

A. July   (global pressures)

B. January   (global winds)

Figure 14.10

59. low

60. high

61. In general, during the winter the cold air over continents is dense and exerts a high pressure while during the summer the warm air over land is less dense and exerts less pressure.

62. The air temperatures over oceans are more uniform throughout the year.

63. highest; lowest

64. In a cyclone, because air with less pressure will have a greater tendency to raise. As air rises it will expand and cool adiabatically, perhaps reaching the dew-point temperature, forming clouds, and producing precipitation.

65. see completed Figure 14.11

Northern Hemisphere

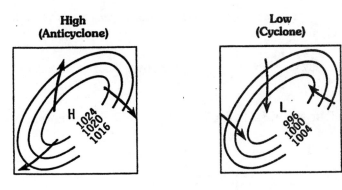

Southern Hemisphere

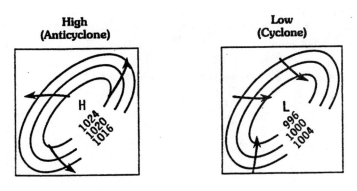

Figure 14.11

66. Northern Hemisphere high: out of; subside; clockwise
Northern Hemisphere low: into; rise; counterclockwise

Southern Hemisphere high: out of; subside; counterclockwise
Southern Hemisphere low: into; rise; clockwise

67. The difference in surface air movement between Northern and Southern Hemisphere anticyclones is in direction; clockwise in the Northern Hemisphere and counterclockwise in the Southern Hemisphere.

68. see completed Figure 14.10

69. winter

70. summer

71. Air moves from areas of higher pressure to areas of lower pressure. Higher pressure over continents during the winter causes air to move from the continent to the ocean. Lower pressure over continents during the summer causes air to move from the oceans to the continents.

72. Summer season: In general, evaporation over the ocean adds water vapor to the air which in turn moves over the continent, increasing the potential for precipitation.

Winter season: In general, since the air originates over the land it contains less water vapor, therefore less potential for precipitation.

73. The seasonal shift in pressure belts and global winds follows the movement of the overhead noon sun throughout the year.

For Web-based laboratory experiences related to this exercise, make sure you have your students investigate our Website at:

http://www.prenhall.com/earthsciencelab

ANSWERS TO EXERCISE FOURTEEN SUMMARY/REPORT PAGE QUESTIONS

1. a) evaporation; b) warm; c) increase; d) 100%; e) released; f) cools, expansion; g) highest

2. 3°C

3. The psychrometer consists of two thermometers, a dry-bulb thermometer and a wet-bulb thermometer which has a piece of wet cloth wrapped around its bulb. As the instrument is spun, evaporation from the cloth on the wet-bulb thermometer lowers the temperature reading. The drier the air, the more evaporation, and hence the greater the difference between the temperature readings of the dry- and wet-bulb thermometers. Using the readings from the two thermometers, a chart can be used to determine the relative humidity.

4. During the adiabatic process rising air cools by expansion. If the air should cool to the dew-point temperature or below, condensation may take place.

5. 1,000 meters

6. 3, 1, 4, 2

7. see completed Figure 14.12

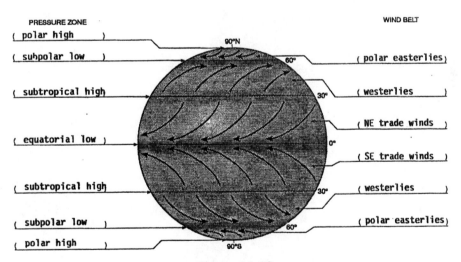

Figure 14.12

8. see completed Figure 14.13

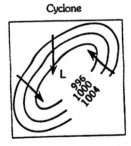
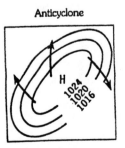

Figure 14.13

ATMOSPHERIC MOISTURE, PRESSURE, AND WIND   115

NOTES:

116

Exercise Fifteen
Air Masses, the Middle-Latitude Cyclone, and Weather Maps

MATERIALS REQUIRED

The following materials are necessary to complete this exercise and should be available in the laboratory. The quantities depend upon the number of students in the laboratory and whether or not students are to work independently or in groups.

United States map or atlas

TEXTBOOK REFERENCES

Tarbuck and Lutgens, *Earth Science*, 10th edition, 2002. Chapter 18

Tarbuck and Lutgens, *Earth Science*, 9th edition, 1999. Chapter 17

Lutgens and Tarbuck, *Foundations of Earth Science*, 3rd edition, 1999. Chapter 14

Murphy and Nance, *Earth Science Today*, 2001. Chapter 12

Skinner and Porter, *The Blue Planet*, 2nd edition, 1999. Chapters 12 and 13

Thompson and Turk, *Earth Science and the Environment*, 2nd edition, 1999. Chapter 16

PROCEDURES AND STRATEGIES

- Most students should have no difficulty completing the exercise within the time allotted for a normal laboratory session. However, if you wish to conserve laboratory time, questions 1 through 29 could be assigned as pre-lab activities.

- Since a United States map or atlas are the only additional materials required to complete the exercise, the entire exercise could be assigned as homework for completion outside the normal laboratory session.

- The most time consuming section of the exercise involves plotting weather station data on Figure 15.6. To conserve time, about 50% of the stations have already been plotted and the minimum number of stations necessary to achieve the goal are presented. Because so few stations have been used to construct the map, students may respond with slightly different interpretations.

- Question 33, which requires students to make forecasts for several cities using their weather map, offers an opportunity to discuss the variables and possibilities that meteorologists must consider when making weather predictions.

ANSWERS TO EXERCISE FIFTEEN QUESTIONS

1. c: continental, designates land; m: maritime, indicates water
    P: polar, air mass originates in high latitudes; T: tropical, air mass originates in low latitudes

2. see completed Figure 15.1

    cP: central and northern Canada
    cT: southwestern United States and northern Mexico
    mP: North Pacific off western Canada and North Atlantic off eastern Canada
    mT: North Pacific off western Mexico and Gulf of Mexico

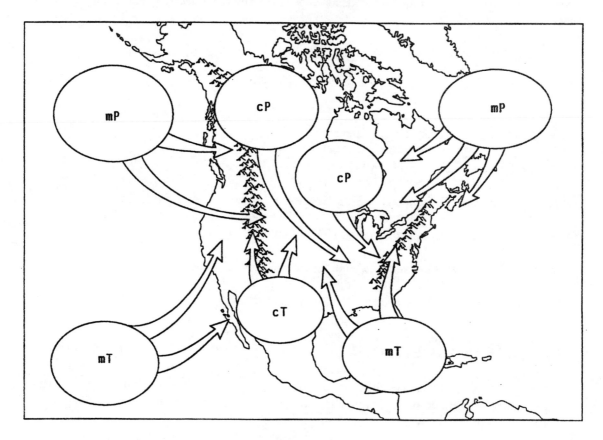

Figure 15.1

3. cP: cold, dry; mP: cool, moist; mT: warm, moist

4. west to east

5. nearly the same, follows the westerlies

6. cP and mT

7. mT

8. mP

9. north and central United States

10. cP; mT

11. cold

12. cold

13. warm front; Explanation: warm air rises gradually over cool air forming stratus clouds which cover a more extensive area than the narrow band of vertical clouds which form along a cold front

14. cold

15. Clear; cold and subsiding air will not expand, cool, and reach its dew-point temperature

16. cold

17. warm

18. see completed Figure 15.3

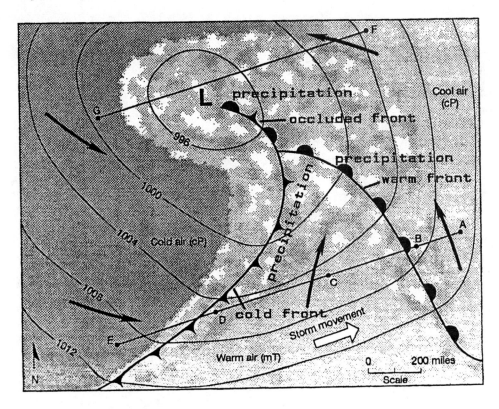

Figure 15.3

19. converging

20. rising; the potential for condensation and precipitation will be good because as air rises adiabatic cooling will occur and the dew-point temperature may be reached

21. falling

22. south

23. wind will be from the northwest and the barometer will rise

24. increase

25. decrease

26. A - B: low stratus clouds, perhaps precipitation, wind from the southeast, barometric pressure is falling; C: wind from the south, warm and perhaps humid air; D: vertical clouds, perhaps thunderstorms; D - E: barometric pressure is rising, wind from the northwest, cool or cold, and clearing sky

27. occluded; a) it is lifted above the cool air; b) as the warm air rises it will expand, adiabatic cooling will occur, and the dew-point temperature may be reached

28. clear, cool or cold in the winter

29. winter; greater

30. Percent of sky cover: five-tenths (50%)
Wind direction: from the northeast
Wind speed: 9 - 14 mph
Temperature: 50°F
Dew-point temperature: 42°F
Barometric pressure: 1019.6 millibars
Barometric change in past 3 hours: 1.8 mb higher
Weather during the past 6 hours: rain

31. see completed station symbol shown below

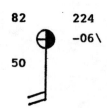

32.   see completed Figure 15.6

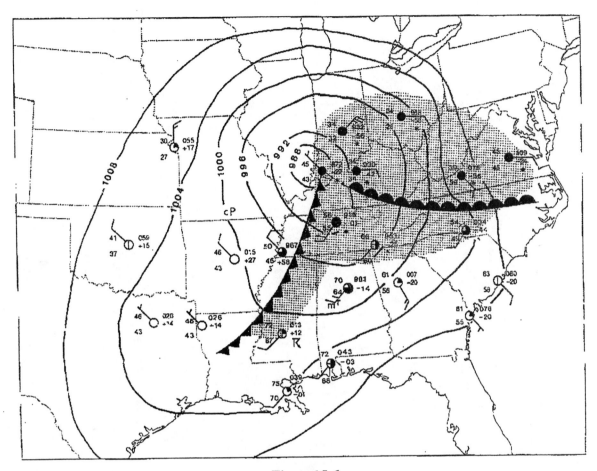

Figure 15.6

33.   Chattanooga, TN: cooler temperature, wind from the northwest, chance of rain, cloudy, steady to rising barometric pressure

Little Rock, AR: cooler temperature, wind from the northwest, clear, rising barometric pressure

Washington, DC: warming, wind from the southeast, rain followed by clearing sky, steady to falling barometric pressure

Raleigh, NC: warmer temperature, wind from the southeast, clearing sky, steady to falling barometric pressure

For Web-based laboratory experiences related to this exercise, make sure you have your students investigate our Website at:

http://www.prenhall.com/earthsciencelab

NOTES:

ANSWERS TO EXERCISE FIFTEEN SUMMARY/REPORT PAGE QUESTIONS

1. cP: central and northern Canada, cold, dry
    mT: North Pacific west of Mexico and Gulf of Mexico, warm, moist
    mP: North Pacific off western Canada and North Atlantic off eastern Canada, cool, moist

2. see the following diagram

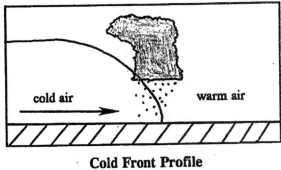

Cold Front Profile

3. a) cold; b) warm; c) cold; d) cold; e) warm; f) cold; g) occluded; h) warm

4. stratus clouds with possible precipitation, warm front passes, temperature rises, wind from the south, cold front, possible thunderstorms, temperature drops, wind from the northwest, clear sky

5. see completed Figure 15.7

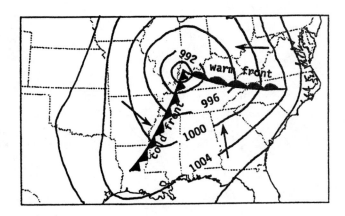

Figure 15.7

6. Little Rock, AR: cooler temperature, wind from the northwest, clear, rising barometric pressure

NOTES:

124

Exercise Sixteen
Global Climates and the Human Impact

MATERIALS REQUIRED

The following materials are necessary to complete this exercise and should be available in the laboratory. The quantities depend upon the number of students in the laboratory and whether or not students are to work independently or in groups.

world map or atlas

TEXTBOOK REFERENCES

Tarbuck and Lutgens, *Earth Science*, 10th edition, 2002. Chapter 19 and Appendix F

Tarbuck and Lutgens, *Earth Science*, 9th edition, 1999. Chapter 18 and Appendix F

Lutgens and Tarbuck, *Foundations of Earth Science*, 3nd edition, 2002. None

Murphy and Nance, *Earth Science Today*, 2001. None

Skinner and Porter, *The Blue Planet*, 2nd edition, 1999. Chapters 14, 20 and Appendix E

Thompson and Turk, *Earth Science and the Environment*, 2nd edition, 1999. Chapters 17, 18 and 19

PROCEDURES AND STRATEGIES

- Most students should have no difficulty completing this exercise within the time allotted for a normal laboratory session.

- Since a world map or atlas are the only additional materials required to complete the exercise, the entire exercise could be assigned as homework for completion outside the normal laboratory session.

- Prior to beginning the laboratory session, a discussion of the value and types of climate classifications and a brief review of climographs, how to prepare them and their uses, may be beneficial.

- Question 42 requires students to determine the climatic classification of Quito, Ecuador. Some students may require assistance in working through the sequence of classification steps.

ANSWERS TO EXERCISE SIXTEEN QUESTIONS

1. June

2. January

3. 10°C

4. 480 millimeters

5. Northern (warmest months are June, July, and August)

6. summer

7. answers to Table 16.2

Climate Group Name		Temperature and/or Precipitation Characteristics
A:	humid tropical	average temperature of coldest month is 18°C or higher
B:	dry climates	potential evaporation exceeds precipitation
C:	humid mid-latitude with mild winters	average temperature of coldest month below 18°C and above -3°C
D:	humid mid-latitude with severe winters	average temperature of coldest month is -3°C or below; warmest month greater than 10°C
E:	polar climates	average temperature of warmest month is below 10°C

8. average temperature of the coldest month is 18°C or higher

9. see completed Figure 16.2

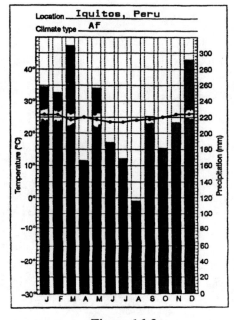

Figure 16.2

10. 2.3°C

11. temperature remains fairly uniform throughout the year

12. approximately 102 inches

13. distributed throughout the year with slightly more during December - February

14. equatorial (tropics)

15. in the interiors

16. Rising, hot air because fronts (boundaries between warm and cold air) do not occur in the tropics

17. 1) average annual precipitation
    2) average annual temperature
    3) seasonal distribution of temperature

18. BW: arid or desert; BS: semiarid or steppe

19. subsidence of air and marked stability of the subtropical high pressures found at these latitudes

20. positions in the deep interiors of large landmasses, far removed from the oceans

21. approximately 20° to 30° North and South latitudes

22. Arabian Peninsula, Pakistan, central Australia, north central Mexico

23. average temperature of the coldest month is below 18°C and above -3°C

24. see completed Figure 16.4

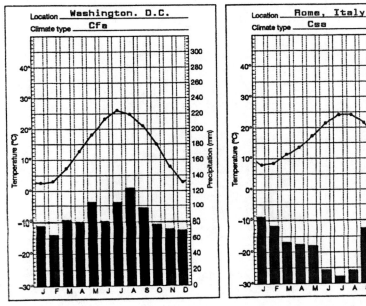

Figure 16.4

25. warmest months are from April to September with similar average temperatures

26. summer is the wet season in Washington, while the precipitation for Rome is concentrated in the late fall and winter

27. Cs climates have at least three times as much precipitation in a winter month as in the driest summer month; precipitation in driest summer month less than 4 centimeters. In Cf climates the criteria for s (or w) cannot be met.

28. Weather fronts

29. India, Burma, China, South Korea, Japan

30. Brazil, Uruguay, Argentina, South Africa, Australia

31. California

32. average temperature of coldest month is -3°C or below; average temperature of warmest month is greater than 10°C

33. see completed Figure 16.5

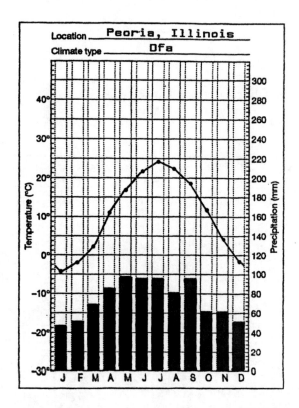

Figure 16.5

34. 28.3°C

35. much greater than Iquitos and greater than Rome

36. In Peoria, more precipitation occurs in summer; while in Rome, precipitation is more plentiful in late fall and winter.

37. Asia (northern)

38. Northern

39. the influence of large expanses of land at higher latitudes in the Northern Hemisphere

40. average temperature of the warmest month is below 10°C

41. ET climates: ET (tundra) climates are slightly warmer than EF climates and are located along coasts at high latitudes

     EF: climates: EF (ice cap) climates are cold and found in the interiors of continents (Greenland and Antarctica) at high latitudes

42. Climate of Quito, Ecuador: C (or Csb)

     Criteria: average temperature of the coldest month is below 18°C and above -3°C; (at least three times as much precipitation in a winter month as in the driest summer month, precipitation in the driest summer month less than 4 centimeters; no month above 22°C, at least 4 months over 10°C)

43. Quito's highland location on the equator has changed its expected A climate to a C climate.

44. Tropical vegetation could not tolerate the colder temperatures and drier conditions found at Quito.

45. Asia

46. Primary pollutants: pollutants are emitted directly from identifiable sources

     Secondary pollutants: pollutants are produced in the atmosphere when certain chemical reactions take place among the primary pollutants

47. transportation; 58.5 million metric tons/year

48. Carbon monoxide; 50%

49. 126.6 million metric tons/year

50. Prior to 1970 the illustrated pollutants all show a general increase.

51. Since 1970 there has been a decrease in the six principal pollutants.

52. In 1970 the Clean Air Act, originally signed into law in 1963, was amended and enforced. This has rersulted in a significant reduction in the atmospheric polutants illustrated on the graph.

53. Approximately 12% (38 ppm/315 ppm x 100)

54. Global warming would result in an average rise of the Earth's sea level due to thermal expansion of water and the melting of glacial ice sheets. Furthermore, global warming and climate change pose a significant risk to human health, the environment, and the economy. Climate-induced changes can add to existing stresses caused by other influences, such as population growth, land-use changes, and pollution, and can create new stresses. Other consequences could include a more vigorous hydrologic cycle with an increase in the possibility of extreme rainfall events and droughts are likely to become more frequent and more severe because of increased evaporation rates.

55. There are a number of energy-related improvements that individuals can use to reduce greenhouse gas emissions. They include using home appliances more efficiently, insulating the home, conserve electricity, use automobiles as infrequently as possible. Non-energy improvements include planting trees and recycling.

56. a. Increased: particulate matter, temperature, precipitation, thunderstorm activity, cloudiness, fog, and calms

    Decreased: solar radiation, relative humidity, and wind speed

    b. Particulate matter shows the greatest increase - 10 times more.

    c. Increased frequency of thunderstorms: the urban heating reduces the atmosphere's stability

    Lower wind speed: building are obstacles that impede the flow of air

    Increased precipitation: urban heating reduces the atmosphere's stability, more condensation nuclei and freezing nuclei from industrial discharges, and buildings impede the passage of weather systems causing rain producing processes to linger

For Web-based laboratory experiences related to this exercise, make sure you have your students investigate our Website at:

http://www.prenhall.com/earthsciencelab

ANSWERS TO EXERCISE SIXTEEN SUMMARY/REPORT PAGE QUESTIONS

1. On a climograph, average monthly temperatures are plotted and connected with a single line and average precipitation for each month is represented with a bar.

2. A climates: tropical, warm, and wet
   B climates: dry, desert (arid) or steppe (semiarid)
   C climates: humid, mid-latitude, mild winters
   D climates: humid, mid-latitude, severe winters
   E climates: cold, polar, tundra or ice cap
   H climates: high altitude

3. A climates: equatorial, tropics, subtropics
   B climates: under stable high pressures in the subtropics or the interiors of large landmasses
   C climates: middle latitudes, often along coasts
   D climates: middle to high latitudes in the Northern Hemisphere
   E climates: high latitudes, polar
   H climates: high altitudes

4. Vast areas of northern coniferous forest: D climates
   Smallest annual range of temperature: A climates
   The highest annual precipitation: A climates
   Mean temperature of the warmest month is below 10°C: E climates
   The result of high elevation and mountain slope orientation: H climates
   Potential evaporation exceeds precipitation: B climates
   Very little change in the monthly precipitation and temperature: A climates
   Caused by the subsidence of air beneath high pressure cells: B climates

5. Cities often cause higher temperatures, more precipitation, thunderstorms, fogs, and calms. They also experience less solar radiation, lower relative humidity, and less wind speed.

6. transportation

7. rising sea level, changes in the global pattern of precipitation, changes in agriculture

8. approximately 12%

NOTES:

Exercise Seventeen
Astronomical Observations

MATERIALS REQUIRED

The following materials are necessary to complete this exercise and should be available in the laboratory. The quantities depend upon the number of students in the laboratory and whether or not students are to work independently or in groups.

telescope(s) (optional)

TEXTBOOK REFERENCES

Tarbuck and Lutgens, *Earth Science*, 10th edition, 2002. Chapters 20, 21 and Appendix E

Tarbuck and Lutgens, *Earth Science*, 9th edition, 1999. Chapters 19, 20 and Appendix E

Lutgens and Tarbuck, *Foundations of Earth Science*, 3rd edition, 2002. Chapter 15

Murphy and Nance, *Earth Science Today*, 2001. Chapter 15, 16 and Appendix E

Skinner and Porter, *The Blue Planet*, 2nd edition, 1999. Chapter 2 and Appendix C

Thompson and Turk, *Earth Science and the Environment*, 2nd edition, 1999. Chapter 22 and Appendix E

PROCEDURES AND STRATEGIES

- No formal laboratory time is necessary to complete this exercise. However, due to the nature of the observations, this exercise will require students several weeks to complete. We recommend that the students begin the exercise, or those sections you choose to assign, as early as possible in the term. If you decide to assign only parts of the exercise, to achieve maximum benefit the following recommendations may be helpful.

  1. *Sunset (or sunrise) observations* should begin at least four weeks prior to doing Exercise Twelve, "Earth-Sun Relations."

  2. *Measuring the noon Sun angle* should begin at least four weeks prior to doing Exercise Twelve, "Earth-Sun Relations."

  3. *Moon observations* should begin at least two weeks prior to doing Exercise Twenty, "The Moon and Sun."

  4. *Star observations* should be done in conjunction with the astronomy lecture unit and is not specifically related to any other exercise.

- Should your time and facilities permit, an optional section on *telescopic observation* is included with the exercise. We recommend that this section be done in conjunction with the astronomy lecture unit. This section is not specifically related to any other exercise.

ANSWERS TO EXERCISE SEVENTEEN QUESTIONS

1. student observations of the setting or rising Sun will vary

2. Answers will vary; however, in general, observations made between June 21 and December 22 will illustrate the Sun setting (or rising) further south with each successive observation. Observations made between December 22 and June 21 will show the Sun setting (or rising) further north with each successive observation.

3. student measurements of the noon Sun angle will vary with the date and location

4. answers will vary

5. answers will vary

6. 0.25° per day (approximate)

7. student observations of the Moon will vary

8. answers will vary

9. eastward

10. later

11. west to east

12. specific answers will vary (blue, blue-white, red, yellow)

13. answers will vary from approximately 1 to 2 fist widths per hour depending on hand size

14. westward

15. The rotation of Earth from west to east makes the position of the star appear to move westward (east to west) throughout the night.

16. student sketches of the constellations will vary

17. The stars in the vicinity of Polaris appear to move in circles around Polaris, with the circles becoming larger the farther a star is from Polaris.

18. has moved to the west

19. The counterclockwise revolution of Earth around the sun causes the star to appear to move westward when viewed at the same time over a period of several weeks.

20. answers will vary

21. A refracting telescope (refractor) has a lens as its objective to gather the light while a reflecting telescope (reflector) has a mirror.

22. The size of a telescope is given as the diameter of its objective (either a lens or mirror). A six inch telescope means that the telescope's objective has a diameter of six inches.

23. The magnification of a telescope is increased or decreased by changing the telescope's eyepiece.

24. An electric drive mechanism turns the telescope to compensate for Earth's rotation, thus allowing a celestial object to be tracked automatically for a long period of time.

25. A finderscope is a small, usually low-powered, telescope with a broad field of view that is attached to a larger telescope to help find celestial objects more easily.

26. student sketches and descriptions of celestial objects will vary

27. a. - d. Answers will vary depending on the date and location.

28. Answers will vary depending on the date.

29. Answers will vary depending on the dates selected.

30. a. - c. Answers will vary depending on the date and location.

31. Answers will vary depending on the date.

For Web-based laboratory experiences related to this exercise, make sure you have your students investigate our Website at:

http://www.prenhall.com/earthsciencelab

NOTES:

ANSWERS TO EXERCISE SEVENTEEN SUMMARY/REPORT PAGE QUESTIONS

1. student answers will vary

2. student answers will vary

3. student answers will vary

4. later

5. student answers will vary (blue, blue-white, red, yellow)

6. student answers will vary (approximately 1 to 2 fist widths per hour depending on hand size); The stars appear to move westward (east to west) throughout the night because of the west to east rotation of Earth.

7. student sketches of constellations will vary

NOTES:

Exercise Eighteen
Patterns in the Solar System

MATERIALS REQUIRED

The following materials are necessary to complete this exercise and should be available in the laboratory. The quantities depend upon the number of students in the laboratory and whether or not students are to work independently or in groups.

    4-meter length of adding machine paper
    meterstick

TEXTBOOK REFERENCES

Tarbuck and Lutgens, *Earth Science*, 10th edition, 2002. Chapters 20 and 21

Tarbuck and Lutgens, *Earth Science*, 9th edition, 1999. Chapters 19 and 20

Lutgens and Tarbuck, *Foundations of Earth Science*, 3rd edition, 2002. Chapter 15

Murphy and Nance, *Earth Science Today*, 2001. Chapter 15

Skinner and Porter, *The Blue Planet*, 2nd edition, 1999. Chapter 2

Thompson and Turk, *Earth Science and the Environment*, 2nd edition, 1999. Chapters 22 and 23

PROCEDURES AND STRATEGIES

- Most students should have no difficulty completing the exercise within the time allotted for a normal laboratory session.

- The exercise requires students to construct both distance and size scale models using a length of adding machine paper. To accomplish the task, we recommend that students work in groups of 4 to 6.

- For those with limited facilities, or if you wish to conserve laboratory time, either, or both, the distance and size scale models can be eliminated and the exercise assigned as homework to be completed outside the scheduled laboratory session.

ANSWERS TO EXERCISE EIGHTEEN QUESTIONS

1. Students are to draw a line between Mars and Jupiter on the upper and lower portions of Table 18.1 and label the line "Belt of Asteroids."

2. Pluto (17°12') and Mercury (7°00')

3. 4 degrees

4. The rotating nebula from which the planets formed became a flattened disk and the orbits of the planets lie nearly in the plane of the disk.

5. See distance scale model of the solar system prepared by students on a piece of adding machine paper.

6. belt of asteroids

7. Spacing of the terrestrial planets: close, largest space is between Earth and Mars, about 5 centimeters (49 million miles)

   Spacing of the Jovian planets: widely spaced, smallest space is between Jupiter and Saturn, about 40 centimeters (403 million miles)

8. In general, with increasing distance from the Sun the space between successive planets be comes increasingly larger.

9. The space between Neptune and Pluto varies the most from the general pattern.

10. See Table 18.2 data below and the diameter scale model of the planets prepared by students on a piece of adding machine paper.

Table 18.2

	Radius in km	Scale Model Radius
Mercury	2,479	1.2 cm
Venus	6,056	3.0 cm
Earth	6,376	3.2 cm
Mars	3,394	1.7 cm
Jupiter	71,500	36.0 cm
Saturn	60,500	30.3 cm
Uranus	23,500	11.8 cm
Neptune	23,265	11.7 cm
(Sun	675,000	337.5 cm)

11. Earth; 7,920 miles

12. Neptune; 28,900 miles

13. Neptune; 3.6 times

14. The diameters of the terrestrial planets: small, the largest is Earth with a diameter of 7,900 miles

    The diameters of the Jovian planets: large, the smallest is Neptune with a diameter of 28,900 miles and the largest is Jupiter with a diameter of 88,700 miles

15. The terrestrial planets are small compared to the Jovian planets.

16. The Sun is <u>106</u> times larger than Earth and <u>9</u> times larger than Jupiter.

17. terrestrial

18. a) Jupiter; 318; b) Mercury; 0.056

19. Jupiter, because it has the greatest mass

20. Mercury, because it is the least massive and therefore would exert the least pull of gravity

21. the Jovian planets, because they have the greatest mass and therefore the greatest pull of gravity

22. The terrestrial planets are all much less massive than the Jovian planets.

23. see completed Figure 18.2

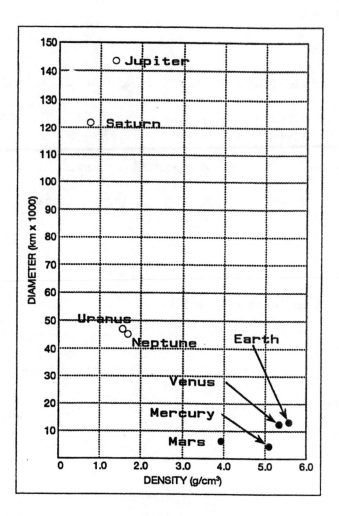

Figure 18.2

24. The smaller, terrestrial planets are all at least twice as dense as the larger Jovian planets.

25. greater

26. rocky

27. Earth's interior must have a density greater than 3.0 g/cm³ to account for the 5.5 g/cm³ average density.

28. Saturn (0.70 g/cm³)

29. The densities of the Jovian planets range from less than the density of water (Saturn, 0.70g/cm³) to approximately 1.6 times greater than the density of water (Neptune).

30. frozen ice and gas

31. Although Jupiter is a very massive planet, the fact that it is essentially a gas object causes it to have a low average density.

32. The densities of the terrestrial planets are at least twice those of the Jovian planets.

33. The terrestrial planets are solid, rocky planets, while the Jovian planets are essentially gas objects.

34. terrestrial; Jovian: small; ice and frozen gas

35. The terrestrial planets have few, or no, moons while the Jovian planets all have multiple moon systems.

36. The more massive Jovian planets have more moons.

37. 243 days on Venus; 9^h50^m on Jupiter

38. The terrestrial planets have long periods of rotation compared to the Jovian planets.

39. 280,000 miles/10 hours = 28,000 mi/hr

40. 1,000 miles/hour (24,000 miles/24 hours)

41. 28 times

42. terrestrial: long days; short years
    Jovian: short days; long years

43. Mercury: 4.2 revolutions in one Earth year
    Neptune: 1/165 of a revolution in one Earth year

44. about 1 day per year

45. about 1.5 Mercury days in one Mercury year

46. If a planet's period of rotation was the same as its period of revolution it would keep the same side toward the Sun throughout its year.

47. Kepler's first law: The path of each planet around the Sun is an ellipse with the Sun at one focus.

Kepler's second law: Each planet revolves so that an imaginary line connecting it to the Sun sweeps over equal areas in equal intervals of time.

Kepler's third law: The orbital periods of the planets and their distances to the Sun are proportional. (orbital period in Earth years)^2 = (distance in AU)^3

48. change

49. 8 Earth years;

> Step 1) $(4 \text{ AU})^3$ = (orbital period)^2;
> Step 2) 64 = (orbital period)^2;
> Step 3) orbital period = the square root of 64;
> Step 4) orbital period = 8 Earth years]

For Web-based laboratory experiences related to this exercise, make sure you have your students investigate our Website at:

http://www.prenhall.com/earthsciencelab

ANSWERS TO EXERCISE EIGHTEEN SUMMARY/REPORT PAGE QUESTIONS

1. see completed Figure 18.3

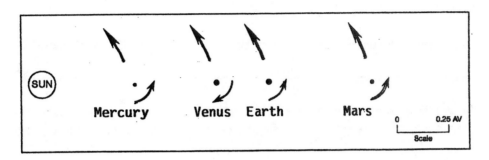

Figure 18.3

2. In general, with increasing distance from the Sun the space between successive planets becomes increasingly larger.

3. Terrestrial planets: the solid, rocky, inner planets; Mercury, Venus, Earth, and Mars

   Jovian planets: the outer, gas planets with central cores of ices and rock; Jupiter, Saturn, Uranus, and Neptune

   Plane of the ecliptic: the imaginary plane that connects Earth's orbit with the celestial sphere in which the orbits of all the planets nearly lie

   Rotation: the spinning of a body, such as Earth, about its axis

   Mass: a measure of the quantity of matter an object contains

   Astronomical unit: a unit for measuring distance within the solar system defined as the average distance from the Sun to Earth (93 million miles or 150 million kilometers)

4. All of the planets formed within a single, large rotating nebula. The counterclockwise revolution of the planets around the Sun is the direction of rotation of the nebula that has been retained by the planets.

5. Diameter: the diameters of the terrestrial planets are small compared to the Jovian planets

    Density: the densities of the terrestrial planets are all greater than those of the Jovian planets

    Period of rotation: the rotational periods of the terrestrial planets are longer than those of the Jovian planets

    Number of moons: the terrestrial planets have fewer moons than the Jovian planets

    Mass: the masses of the terrestrial planets are all less than those of the Jovian planets

6. Knowing the distance of a planet from the Sun and using Kepler's third law, the period of revolution of a planet can be calculated using the equation (orbital period in Earth years)^2 = (distance in AU).

Exercise Nineteen
Planet Positions

MATERIALS REQUIRED

The following materials are necessary to complete this exercise and should be available in the laboratory. The quantities depend upon the number of students in the laboratory and whether or not students are to work independently or in groups.

no instructor supplied materials are necessary

TEXTBOOK REFERENCES

Tarbuck and Lutgens, *Earth Science*, 10th edition, 2002. Chapters 20 and 21

Tarbuck and Lutgens, *Earth Science*, 9th edition, 1999. Chapters 19 and 20

Lutgens and Tarbuck, *Foundations of Earth Science*, 3rd edition, 2002. Chapter 15

Murphy and Nance, *Earth Science Today*, 2001. Chapter 15

Skinner and Porter, *The Blue Planet*, 2nd edition, 1999. Chapter 2

Thompson and Turk, *Earth Science and the Environment*, 2nd edition, 1999. Chapters 22 and 23

PROCEDURES AND STRATEGIES

- Most students should have no difficulty completing the exercise within the time allotted for a normal laboratory session.

- Students may require some assistance in determining the positions of the planets for "today's date" or a date specified by the instructor. As a point of information, when calculating the number of days that have elapsed since the charts were draw (December 31, 1957) make sure to include leap years. We recommend that the number of elapsed days and years be calculated by the class as a group so that all the students will be using the same numbers when they calculate the new positions of the planets.

- Since no additional materials are required, the entire exercise could be assigned as homework for completion outside the normal laboratory session.

ANSWERS TO EXERCISE NINETEEN QUESTIONS

1. (arrows showing the direction of revolution of each planet drawn by students on Figures 19.1-19.3 will all be counterclockwise)

2. counterclockwise

3. Mercury: 88 days; Mars: 687 days; Saturn: 29.5 years

4. Mercury: 88 days
   Venus: 224.7 days
   Mars: 687 days
   Jupiter: 11.86 years
   Saturn: 29.46 years

5. Venus: 84°
   Earth: 100°
   Mars: 225°
   Jupiter: 199°
   Saturn: 257°

6. Venus: Aquarius
   Mars: Libra
   Saturn: Scorpius

NOTE: When answering question 7 it is important to remember to advance Earth 90 days beyond its December 31, 1957 position.

7. Mercury: Aries (90 days after December 31, 1957)
   Jupiter: Virgo (90 days after December 31, 1957)

8. Mercury's location has changed considerably (nearly 180° from where it was on December 31, 1957) while Jupiter's location has not changed at all.

9. 4.2 revolutions (365.25 divided by 88)

10. 1/11.86 (0.08) of a revolution

11. considerably; slightly

12. see completed Figure 19.4

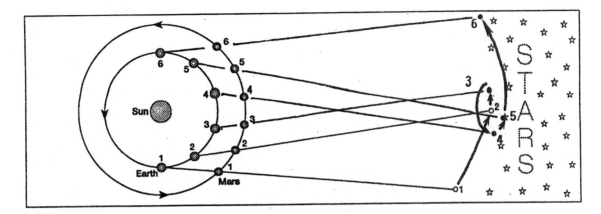

Figure 19.4

13. Mars appears to move forward, then backward, and then forward again in its orbit as viewed from Earth.

14. No

15. The fact that Earth catches up to and then passes Mars in its orbit makes it appear that Mars moves backward.

16. If it is assumed that Earth does not move in its orbit, then the observed motion of Mars must be explained as "real" motion, i.e. Mars must move in small circular orbits as it also orbits Earth in a larger orbit. The result, when observed from a non-moving Earth, would be that Mars would periodically move backward in its orbit.

17. answers and data recorded in Table 19.1 will vary with the date selected

18. answers will vary with the date selected

19. answers will vary with the date selected

For Web-based laboratory experiences related to this exercise, make sure you have your students investigate our Website at:

http://www.prenhall.com/earthsciencelab

NOTES:

ANSWERS TO EXERCISE NINETEEN SUMMARY/REPORT PAGE QUESTIONS

1. figure will vary with the date selected

2. answers will vary with the date selected

3. A planet will periodically exhibit retrograde motion when it is viewed from Earth, as Earth catches up to and passes the planet.

4. A planet being "in" a particular constellation refers to the pattern of stars that form the background behind the planet when the planet is viewed from Earth.

5. Saturn, with a 29.46 year period of revolution, only moves 1/29.46 of a revolution each year. This small distance, about 12° in the sky, causes its position to change only slightly from year to year.

6. To be visible from Earth, Mars must be positioned on either side of the Sun relative to Earth, or on the opposite side of Earth from the Sun. If Mars is positioned on the opposite side of the Sun from Earth it will not be visible from Earth.

7. see completed Figure 19.6

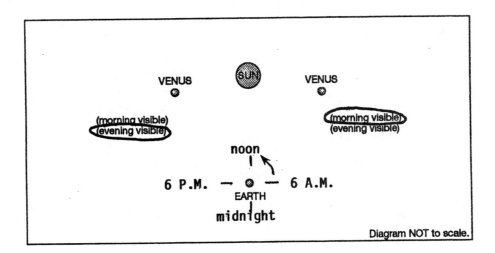

Figure 19.6

NOTES:

152

Exercise Twenty
The Moon and Sun

MATERIALS REQUIRED

The following materials are necessary to complete this exercise and should be available in the laboratory. The quantities depend upon the number of students in the laboratory and whether or not students are to work independently or in groups.

lunar globe (optional)　　　　　sandbox
sand　　　　　　　　　　　　meterstick
small balls (various sizes and densities)

> **NOTE:** 1) Although not necessary to complete the exercise, students may find a lunar globe interesting and helpful.
>
> 2) Students may find a hand lens useful when working with Figure 20.7, a lunar surface photograph.

TEXTBOOK REFERENCES

Tarbuck and Lutgens, *Earth Science*, 10th edition, 2002. Chapters 20, 21 and 22

Tarbuck and Lutgens, *Earth Science*, 9th edition, 1999. Chapters 19, 20 and 21

Lutgens and Tarbuck, *Foundations of Earth Science*, 3rd edition, 1999. Chapter 15

Murphy and Nance, *Earth Science Today*, 2001. Chapters 15 and 16

Skinner and Porter, *The Blue Planet*, 2nd edition, 1999. Chapters 2 and 3

Thompson and Turk, *Earth Science and the Environment*, 2nd edition, 1999. Chapters 23 and 24

PROCEDURES AND STRATEGIES

- Most students should have no difficulty completing the exercise within the time allotted for a normal laboratory session.

- Since no additional materials are required, the entire exercise could be assigned as homework for completion outside the normal laboratory session.

ANSWERS TO EXERCISE TWENTY QUESTIONS

1. see completed Figure 20.2

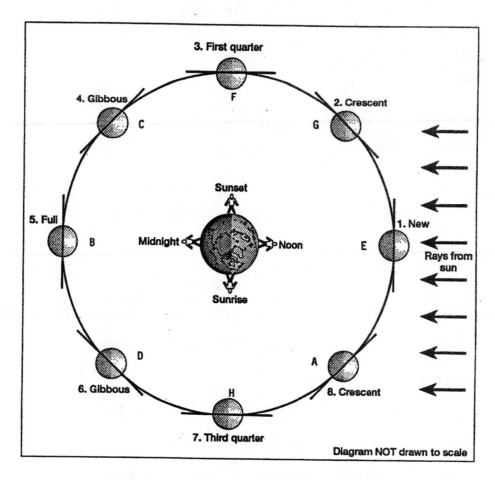

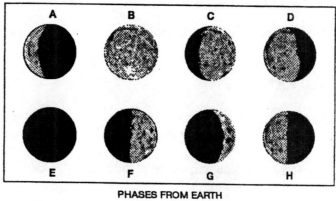

PHASES FROM EARTH

Figure 20.2

2. increasing

3. decreasing

4.

Position	Letter of Phase	Name of Phase	
1.	E	New	(see completed Figure 20.2)
2.	G	Crescent	
3.	F	First quarter	
4.	C	Gibbous	
5.	B	Full	
6.	D	Gibbous	
7.	H	Third quarter	
8.	A	Crescent	

5. noon

6. midnight

7. eastward; later

8. No, the Moon is on the opposite side of Earth from the observer.

9. sunset; eastward

10. Yes, during the first- and third-quarter phases the Moon is overhead at sunset and sunrise and there fore can be observed during the daylight hours.

11. Rise: noon (approximate); Set: midnight (approximate)

12. Rise: midnight (approximate); Set: noon (approximate)

13. later; larger (when the crescent Moon is observed in the early evening in the western sky the phase of the Moon is between new- and first-quarter)

14. see completed Figure 20.3

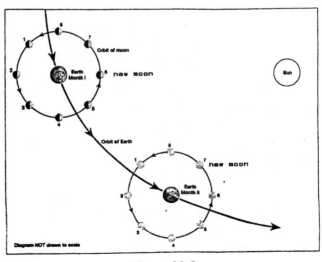

Figure 20.3

15.

Phase	Lunar Position (Month I)
New-moon	6
Third quarter	4
Full-moon	2
First quarter	8

16. see completed Figure 20.3

17. 3; see completed Figure 20.3

18. 6

19. sidereal; 27.3

20. before

21. synodic; 29.5

22. A sidereal month is one complete 360° revolution of the moon around Earth. During a synodic month the Moon completes a complete cycle of phases. The synodic month is approximately two days longer than the sidereal month because of the motion of the Earth-Moon system around the Sun.

23. see completed Figure 20.4

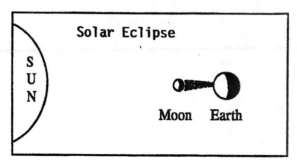

Figure 20.4

Description: A solar eclipse occurs when the Moon moves in a line directly between the Earth and Sun and the dark shadow of the moon is cast on Earth.

24. new-moon

25. see completed Figure 20.5

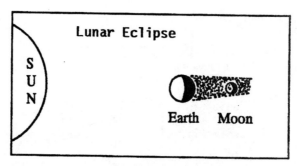

Figure 20.5

Description: A lunar eclipse occurs when the Moon moves into the shadow of Earth on the opposite side of Earth from the Sun.

26. full-moon

27. For an eclipse to occur the Moon's orbit must lay exactly along the plane of the ecliptic. Because the Moon's orbit is inclined about 5° to the plane the exact alignment happens only occasionally.

28. Maria form when very fluid basaltic lava floods a large impact crater.

29. 40

30. Mare Crisium; 400 km

31. Latitude: 10°N; longitude: 20°W

32.

	Location	Type of Feature
Sinus Iridum:	45°N, 32°W	old lava-flooded crater
Humbolt:	26°S, 80°E	large impact crater
Mare Orientale:	19°S, 93°W	mare
Rupes Altai:	23°S, 23°E	fault scarp
Kepler:	8°N, 38°W	youthful crater with rays

33. maria

34. older

35. younger

36. older

37. (the small crater overlapping the lower edge of the large crater is the youngest)

38. younger

39. Youngest: unnamed crater northwest of Hainzel
             Hainzel
    Oldest: Mee

40. Copernicus appears to be a youthful rayed crater

41. Mee appears to be older than Tycho

42. youthful crater with rays

43. The rays, which indicate an impact origin for the crater, are fragmented material that was ejected from the crater at the time of impact.

44. On Earth erosion has removed much of the surface evidence.

45. The height from which the balls are dropped

46. Mass and velocity have the greatest influence on the size and depth of the craters. (Note: the kenetic energy (KE) of each sphere as it strikes the surface is equal to 0.5 x mass of the ball (m) x velocity of the ball, squared (v^2): $KE = 0.5mv^2$)

47. (answers will vary depending on the hypothesis)

48. see completed Figure 20.9

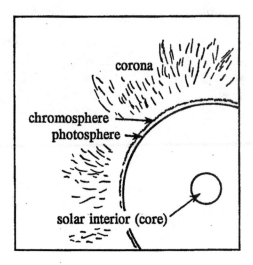

Figure 20.9

49. Photosphere: The visible surface of the Sun that radiates energy to space. It has a grainy appearance, contains most of the elements found on Earth, and has an average temperature of about 6000 K (10,000°F).

Chromosphere: The relatively thin (a few thousand kilometers thick), red rim of hot, incandescent gases (primarily hydrogen with some helium) just above the photosphere.

Corona: The tenuous, outermost portion of the solar atmosphere consisting of ionized gases that extends a million kilometers from the Sun. Its temperature exceeds 1 million K at the top.

50. 91 millimeters; 9560 miles/millimeter

51. Hot gases rising from below produce numerous bright spots called granules. As the gas spreads laterally, it cools and darkens, sinks back into the interior, and gives the photosphere the appearance of boiling. This up-and-down movement of gas gives the solar surface a grainy appearance.

52. approximately 67,000 miles (7 millimeters x 9560 miles/millimeter)

53. Pominences are hugh structures that, when they are on the limb or edge of the Sun, appear as great arches. They appear to be condensations of coronal material "sliding down" lines of magnetic force back into the chromosphere.

54. approximately 10,000 miles

55. see completed Figure 20.11

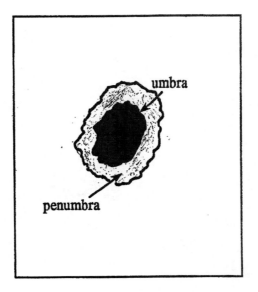

Figure 20.11

56. The temperature of sunspots is about 1500 K less than that of the solar surface. They appear dark only because they are cooler, by contrast, than the photosphere.

For Web-based laboratory experiences related to this exercise, make sure you have your students investigate our Website at:

http://www.prenhall.com/earthsciencelab

NOTES:

ANSWERS TO EXERCISE TWENTY SUMMARY/REPORT PAGE QUESTIONS

1. The phases in the Moon are due to the changing position of the Moon relative to the Earth and Sun allowing varying amounts of the illuminated side of the Moon to be visible from Earth.

2. far left photograph - Phase: crescent (waning); Time: 9 A.M. (approximate)
   left-center photograph - Phase: third quarter; Time: 6 A.M. (sunrise)
   right-center photograph - Phase: gibbous (waning); Time: 3 A.M. (approximate)
   far left photograph - Phase: full; Time: midnight

3. (Figure 20.13 will vary depending on whether or not the lunar observations in Exercise Seventeen, "Astronomical Observations," were assigned and completed by the student. If Exercise Seventeen was not assigned, the diagram will illustrate the position of the Moon during full moon, new moon, first quarter, and third quarter.)

4. The sidereal month, 27 days, is the time that it takes the Moon to complete one 360° revolution around Earth. The synodic month, 29 days, is the time it takes for the moon to complete a cycle of phases. The difference of approximately 2 days is the result of the motion of the Earth-Moon system around the Sun.

5. Terrae, the lunar highlands, are bright and irregular; while maria, the lunar lowlands or "seas," are dark and rather flat.

6. a) mare; b) sharp rim; c) youthful rayed crater; d) material ejected from the crater during its formation

7. When craters overlap, the rim of the most recent crater will cut through the rim of the older.

8. Chromosphere: The relatively thin (a few thousand kilometers thick), red rim of hot, incandescent gases (primarily hydrogen with some helium) just above the photosphere.

   Solar eclipse: A solar eclipse occurs when the Moon moves in a line directly between the Earth and Sun and the dark shadow of the Moon is cast on Earth.

   Sunspot: A sunspot is a dark spot on the solar surface. It appears dark only because its temperature is about 1500 K less than that of the solar surface.

   Lunar terrae: Lunar terrae are the bright, densely cratered lunar highlands.

9. Answers will vary. In general, crater size and depth are related to the mass and velocity of the impacting object.

NOTES:

Exercise Twenty-One
Location and Distance on Earth

MATERIALS REQUIRED

The following materials are necessary to complete this exercise and should be available in the laboratory. The quantities depend upon the number of students in the laboratory and whether or not students are to work independently or in groups.

globe   atlas

world wall map   50-80 cm length of string

> **NOTE**: Exercise Twenty-one involves basic Earth science skills used throughout the manual. Should you decide to do the exercise, we recommend that it is introduced early in the term.

TEXTBOOK REFERENCES

Tarbuck and Lutgens, *Earth Science*, 10th edition, 2002. Appendix B

Tarbuck and Lutgens, *Earth Science*, 9th edition, 1999. Appendix B

Lutgens and Tarbuck, *Foundations of Earth Science*, 3rd edition, 2002. Appendix D

Murphy and Nance, *Earth Science Today*, 12001. None

Skinner and Porter, *The Blue Planet*, 2nd edition, 1999. None

Thompson and Turk, *Earth Science and the Environment*, 2nd edition, 1999. Chapter 15 (inset)

PROCEDURES AND STRATEGIES

- Exercises Twenty-one, "Location and Distance on Earth," and Twenty-two, "The Metric System, Measurements, and Scientific Inquiry," involve basic Earth science skills that are used throughout the manual. Should you decide to do either, or both, exercises, we recommend that they be introduced as early as possible in the term.

- Due to the nature of the material presented, most students will require more time to complete the exercise than that allotted for a normal laboratory period. To conserve laboratory time, sections could be assigned for completion outside the normal laboratory session, or omitted. A globe is required to complete most of the exercise.

- Question 32 requires the student to locate and label features on a world map, Figure 21.8. At your discretion, features could be added to, or deleted from, the list presented.

ANSWERS TO EXERCISE TWENTY-ONE QUESTIONS

1. see completed Figure 21.3

2. see completed Figure 21.3

3. see completed Figure 21.3

4. see completed Figure 21.3

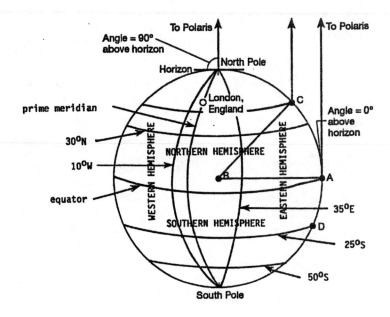

Figure 21.3

5. answers will vary depending on the globe used

6. see completed Figure 21.3

7. a) see completed Figure 21.4
   b) Point C: 55°N; Point D: 35°S; Point E: 0°
   (equator); Point F: 20°N

8. Moscow, Russia: 56°N latitude
   Durban, South Africa: 30°S latitude
   Your home city: answers will vary
   Your college campus city: answers will vary

9. answers will vary

10. 90

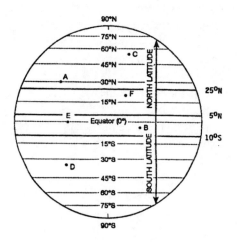

Figure 21.4

11. North Pole and South Pole

12. 66°30'00"N latitude: Arctic Circle
    23°30'00"N latitude: Tropic of Cancer
    23°30'00"S latitude: Tropic of Capricorn
    66°30'00"S latitude: Antarctic Circle

13. 45°

14. In the Northern Hemisphere, the angle of Polaris above the horizon is the same as the latitude of a place.

15. Fairbanks, AK: 65°
    St. Paul, MN: 45°
    New Orleans, LA: 30°
    Your home city: answers will vary
    Your college campus city: answers will vary

16. see completed Figure 21.3

17. see completed Figure 21.3

18. answers will vary depending on the globe used

19. see completed Figure 21.3

20. a) see completed Figure 21.5

    b) Point C: 55°E longitude; Point D: 75°W longitude; Point E: 65°E longitude; Point F: 70°W longitude

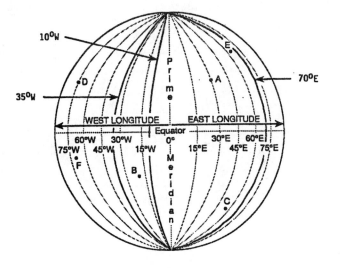

Figure 21.5

21. Wellington, New Zealand: 175°E longitude
    Honolulu, Hawaii: 158°W longitude
    Your home city: answers will vary
    Your college campus city: answers will vary

22. answers will vary

23. 180

24. 11:56 A.M.

25. 12:16 P.M.

26. 72°W longitude: 11:52 A.M.
    65°W longitude: 12:20 P.M.
    90°W longitude: 10:40 A.M.
    110°E longitude: midnight

27. 6:00 P.M.: 90°W longitude (ship's time is 6 hours earlier)
    1:00 A.M.: 165°E longitude (ship's time is 11 hours later)
    2:30 P.M.: 37°30'W longitude (ship's time is 2 hours earlier)

28. Point B: 30°S latitude, 30°W longitude; Point C: 0° latitude, 90°W longitude; Point D: 45°N latitude, 75°W longitude; Point E: 13°N latitude, 27°W longitude

29. See completed Figure 21.7

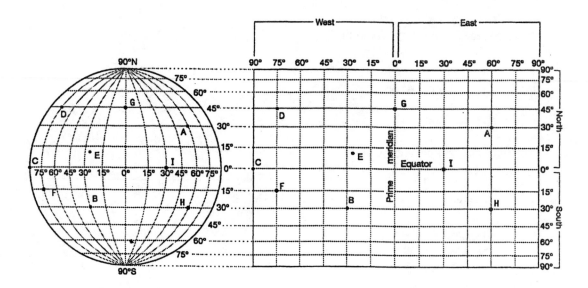

Figure 21.7

30. Kansas City, MO: 39°05'N latitude, 94°35'W longitude
    Miami, FL: 25°45'N latitude, 80°11'W longitude
    Oslo, Norway: 59°56'N latitude, 10°41'E longitude
    Auckland, New Zealand: 36°53'S latitude, 174°45'E longitude
    Quito, Ecuador: 0°17'S latitude, 78°32'W longitude
    Cairo, Egypt: 30°00'N latitude, 31°17'E longitude

31. 19°28'N latitude, 99°09'W longitude: Mexico City, Mexico
    41°52'N latitude, 12°37'E longitude: Rome, Italy
    1°30'S latitude, 33°00'E longitude: Lake Victoria

32. See completed Figure 21.8 (NOTE: Alternate Figure 21.8 is for students who have completed Exercise Nine and HAVE NOT done Exercise Twenty-one)

33. Students are to use a string to investigate great circles on a globe.

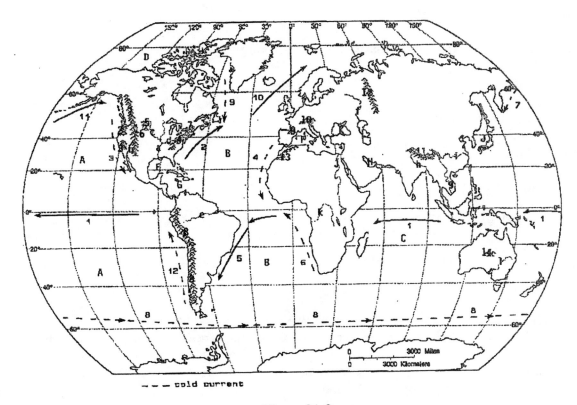

Figure 21.8

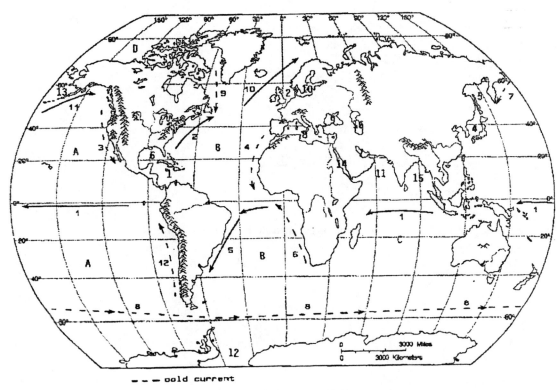

Alternate Figure 21.8

34. equator

35. All meridians, when paired with their opposites, form great circles.

36. All parallels, with the exception of the equator (and poles), are small circles.

37. North and South Poles

38. none

39. Points A-H: great circle; Points D-G: small circle; Points: C-I: great circle; Points B-H: small circle

40. a) great; b) small; c) great; d) points

41. 3,450 miles (5,550 km)

42. 5,717 kilometers (3,554 miles)

43. Degrees along the great circle between Memphis and Tokyo = 93.5°
    Distance along the great circle between Memphis and Tokyo = 6,452 miles (10,379 km)

44. Missouri, Iowa, Nebraska, S. Dakota, N. Dakota, western Canada (Saskatchewan, Alberta, British Columbia, Yukon), Alaska, Kuril Islands

45. the distance becomes shorter

46. 15° latitude: 107.596 km, 66.830 miles
    30° latitude: 96.528 km, 59.955 miles
    45° latitude: 78.880 km, 48.994 miles
    80° latitude: 19.402 km, 12.051 miles

47. D - G: 75° x 48.994 miles/degree (at latitude 45°) = 3,675 miles
    B - H: 90° x 96.528 km/degree (at latitude 30°) = 8,688 km

48. 130° (approximate) (Memphis, 90°W longitude; Tokyo, 140°E longitude)

49. 91.327 km (56.725 miles)

50. 7,374 miles [130° x 56.725 miles/degree (at latitude 35°) = 7,374 miles]

51. The great circle route is 922 miles shorter (7,374 miles - 6,452 miles) (approximate).

For Web-based laboratory experiences related to this exercise, make sure you have your students investigate our Website at:

http://www.prenhall.com/earthsciencelab

ANSWERS TO EXERCISE TWENTY-ONE SUMMARY/REPORT PAGE QUESTIONS

1. see completed Figure 21.11

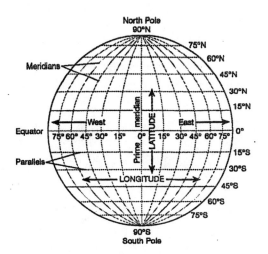

Figure 21.11

Explanation: The location of a point on Earth's surface is given by noting both the point's latitude, North or South, using the parallels of latitude, and its longitude, East or West, using the meridians of longitude.

2. Parallel of latitude: a line of the Earth's grid that extends around Earth in an east-west direction and marks north or south distance from the equator (0° latitude) on Earth's surface

   Meridian of longitude: a line of the Earth's grid that is half of a circle that extends from the North Pole to the South Pole on one side of Earth and marks east or west distance from the prime meridian (0° longitude) on Earth's surface

   Great circle: the largest possible circle that can be drawn on Earth (globe); it divides Earth (globe) into two equal parts, called hemispheres

3. a) F; b) T; c) F

4. In the Northern Hemisphere, the angle of Polaris above the horizon is the same as the latitude of the place.

5. 69 miles (approximate)

6. answers will vary

7. 38°00'N latitude, 23°38'E longitude

8. 922 miles shorter (approximate)

9. 9,764 miles [141.5° (degrees of latitude between London and the South Pole) x 69 miles/degree (miles per degree along a great circle) = 9,764 miles]

10. Your longitude is 60°W [4 hours x 15°/hour, west (your time is earlier) of London]. Examining the globe shows that you are closer to New York (73°58'W longitude) than to London (0° longitude).

NOTES:

Exercise Twenty-Two

The Metric System, Measurements, and Scientific Inquiry

MATERIALS REQUIRED

The following materials are necessary to complete this exercise and should be available in the laboratory. The quantities depend upon the number of students in the laboratory and whether or not students are to work independently or in groups.

metric tape measure
  or meterstick
metric balance
"bathroom" scale (metric)
large graduated cylinder
  (marked in milliliters)

paper clip
nickel coin
paper cup
small rock
thread

NOTE: Exercise Twenty-two involves basic Earth science skills used throughout the manual. Should you decide to do the exercise, we recommend that it be introduced early in the term.

TEXTBOOK REFERENCES

Tarbuck and Lutgens, *Earth Science*, 10th edition, 2001. Introduction and Appendix A

Tarbuck and Lutgens, *Earth Science*, 9th edition, 1999. Introduction and Appendix A

Lutgens and Tarbuck, *Foundations of Earth Science*, 3rd edition, 2002. Introduction and Appendix A

Murphy and Nance, *Earth Science Today*, 2001. Chapter 1 and Appendix A

Skinner and Porter, *The Blue Planet*, 2nd edition, 1999. Introduction and Appendix A

Thompson and Turk, *Earth Science and the Environment*, 2nd edition, 1999. Chapter 1 and Appendix C

PROCEDURES AND STRATEGIES

- Exercises Twenty-one, "Location and Distance on the Earth," and Twenty-two, "The Metric System, Measurements, and Scientific Inquiry," involve basic Earth science skills that are used throughout the manual. Should you decide to do either, or both, exercises, we recommend that they be introduced as early as possible in the term.

- Most students should have no difficulty completing the exercise within the time allotted for a normal laboratory session. However, if you wish to conserve laboratory time, questions 16 through 33 could be assigned as homework to be completed after the scheduled laboratory session, or sections of the exercise could be omitted.

- Prior to beginning the exercise, a brief discussion of the metric system of units may be beneficial.

- Students may require specific instructions on the procedure for using a metric balance.

- The exercise offers an opportunity to discuss how science is done and the method of scientific inquiry.

171

ANSWERS TO EXERCISE TWENTY-TWO QUESTIONS

1. - 6. answers will vary

7. a) 205.0 cm; b) 1500.0 mm; c) 98.1 dl; d) 5400.0 mg; e) 0.0068 km; f) 42.146 m; g) 0.3215 kg; h) 707.3 dal

8. a) answers will vary; b) answers will vary depending on the length of the table measured in question 8a.

9. 1 inch = 2.54 centimeters

10. 1 meter = 3.28 feet

11. 1 mile = 1.61 kilometers

12. 1 gallon = 3.78 liters

13. 1 cubic centimeter = 0.06 cubic inch

14. 1 gram = 0.035 ounce

15. 1 pound = 0.45 kilograms

16. a) -13.3°C; b) 32°F; c) 22.2°C; d) 95°F; e) 37°C; f) 80.6°F; g) 161.6°F; h) 373 K

17. a) no; b) no, not likely; c) yes; d) yes; e) chilly; f) perspiring

18. yes

19. yes

20. no

21. yes

22. yes

23. no

24. no

25. yes

26. no

27. no

28. 1,000

29. 25,000 micrometers on a 2.5 cm line (10,000 micrometers/centimeter x 2.5 centimeters)
    25,000,000 nanometers in a 2.5 cm line (10,000,000 nanometers/centimeter x 2.5 centimeters)

30. 20,000 waves in one centimeter (10,000,000 nanometers/centimeter divided by 500 nanometers per wave)

31. 9.5 AUs from the Sun

32. 9.66 trillion (9,660,000,000,000) kilometers per year

33. 25,620,000,000,000 (25.62 trillion) miles
    41,250,000,000,000 (41.25 trillion) kilometers

34. a. - f., answers will vary

35. answers will vary

36. answers will vary

37. Hypothesis: A person's shoe length is related to their height; in that, as height increases so will shoe length.

38. data in Table 22.2 will vary

39. In general, the points plotted on the graph follow a line.

40. (students are to plot a single line that best fits the points on the graph)

41. As a person's height increases, so does their shoe length.

42. (Knowing a person's height, students are to predict that person's shoe length using the graph in Figure 22.6.)

43. reasonably well

44. Accept. Explanation: Because the data that has been collected and plotted on the graph can be used to make reasonable predictions concerning the relation between a person's height and their shoe length, the hypothesis appears to be valid. (answers may vary depending on data)

45. Using ten thousand people, the line drawn on the graph that best fit the points that were plotted would be more representative and reliable, therefore predictions would be more accurate.

For Web-based laboratory experiences related to this exercise, make sure you have your students investigate our Website at:

http://www.prenhall.com/earthsciencelab

NOTES:

ANSWERS TO EXERCISE TWENTY-TWO SUMMARY/REPORT PAGE QUESTIONS

1. Length: meter (m); Mass: gram (g); Volume: liter (l)

2. a) 20 deciliters; b) 0.600 meter; c) 22.2°C; d) 320 grams; e) 12,000 milligrams

3. a) no; b) yes; c) yes

4. answers will vary

5. 30,000 micrometers in 3.0 centimeters

6. 40,000 waves along a two centimeter line [(10,000,000 nanometers/centimeter x 2 centimeters) divided by 500 nanometers/wave]

7. approximately 62 trillion kilometers

8. 19.1 astronomical units from the Sun (approximate)

9. Density is the mass of a substance per unit volume (g/cc^3); while specific gravity is the ratio of the mass of a given volume of substance to that of an equal volume of some other substance taken as a standard (usually water at 4°C).

10. accepted; Explanation: Because the data that has been collected and plotted on the graph can be used to make reasonable predictions concerning the relation between a person's height and their shoe length, the hypothesis appears to be valid. (answers may vary depending on data)

NOTES: